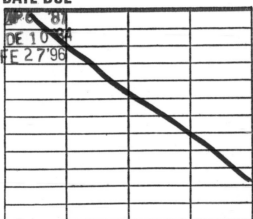

BRIGHAM YOUNG

From the turbulent history of the western migrations comes this thrilling story of a desperate and exalting adventure as Brigham Young led 15,000 persecuted Mormons to religious freedom in Utah, founding an empire in the valley of the Great Salt Lake and bringing a desert to bloom. As a farmer and carpenter in New York State, he tried but failed to find a satisfying religion, until he read the inspiring *Book of Mormon*. When Prophet Joseph Smith was assassinated by a mob, Brigham Young became the Mormon leader and led his penniless, starving, fever-ridden people over the Rocky Mountains to a land where they found safety and freedom from persecution.

Books by Olive Burt

BRIGHAM YOUNG

JEDEDIAH SMITH: Fur Trapper of the Old West

JOHN CHARLES FREMONT: Trail Marker of the Old West

FIRST WOMAN EDITOR: Sarah J. Hale

PETTICOATS WEST

BORN TO TEACH

BRIGHAM YOUNG

BY OLIVE BURT

JULIAN MESSNER

NEW YORK

Published simultaneously in the United States and Canada by
Julian Messner, a division of Simon & Schuster, Inc.,
1 West 39 Street, New York, 10018. All rights reserved.

Eighth Printing, 1968

To Nancy
with Love

Printed in the United States of America
Library of Congress Catalog Card No. 56–10445

CONTENTS

CONTENTS

A FIDDLE CALLS

⋙-⋙-⋙-⋙-⋙-⋙-⋙-⋙-⋙

Swish! Swoosh!

The sickle cut through the meadow grass in long, strong sweeps.

Swish! Swoosh!

Brigham stopped, straightened up and rubbed his soiled hickory shirt sleeve across his forehead to wipe away the sweat.

He was a medium-sized boy of seven, with soft auburn hair that curled gently where it was dampened by sweat. His face was square and determined, even in its childish softness. His eyes were a clear, deep blue that looked straight at things. They were disturbing eyes. Many times his brothers or playmates, telling a childish "story," pretending to something that wasn't so, had found their own gaze shifting away from the penetrating gaze of the little boy.

Swish! Swoosh!

Behind Brigham came his brother Phineas, two years older, gathering the cut grass into small piles, ready for the fork to toss them onto the rickety wagon. Joseph, eleven, handled the fork. He walked beside the wagon and tossed the piled grass onto the flat bed. The bony brown horse waited patiently, stretching his neck to reach the mouthfuls of grass around him.

Brigham stopped cutting again and wiped the trickling

sweat from his face. Phineas, busily raking, looked up at his brother.

"We're almost done, Brig."

Brigham looked at the narrow patch of grass still between him and the gurgling creek. Then he studied the sky, glowing with the colors of sunset. Without a word he bent and swung the scythe again.

Swish! Swoosh!

Phineas raked; Joseph tossed the grass up onto the wagon. There was no talking or joking.

At last it was all cut. Brigham and Phineas helped toss the forkfuls onto the wagon. Then they climbed up on the piled, sweet-smelling grass. Joseph took his place in front, picked up the homemade lines and clucked to the old horse, "Git along, Bony!"

Brigham stretched out on the grass, his hands behind his head, his bare toes wriggling in comfort.

"I'm mighty glad it's Saturday night!" he said, burrowing deeper into the grass.

Phineas nodded. "I sure am, too, Brig. Don't have to work tomorrow! Pa's goin' to take us over to camp meeting to hear that new preacher. Only thing is—" he hesitated a moment, then went on, "we don't have such good meals on Sunday. Everything cooked the day before!"

"Well," Brigham said reasonably, "you know Pa and Ma don't hold with breaking the Sabbath. Do you like to hear them preachers, Phin? You like to hear 'em talk about hell and damnation?"

Phineas squinted up at the slowly darkening sky. "I sure do, Brig. Makes me feel good to know that the Lord is watching me—makes it easier for me to do the right thing."

Brigham thought this over. "I reckon that's right. You know someone's watching, right close, you're going to behave. But it must keep the Lord busy. It 'ud be easier for Him if we watched ourselves, wouldn't it?"

Joseph drove carefully down the rutted road and turned in at the unfenced lot belonging to his father John Young, just outside the little village of Sherburne, New York. This was just one of the homes Brigham had known since his birth in Whittingham, Vermont, on June 1, 1801. The boy couldn't remember the Vermont place; he had been only three when the family moved away. But he could remember other small farms in New York State, where they had lived at different times.

Joseph drove on past the small log house to the pole fence around the barnyard. Here, at one side of the yard, he drew on the lines and Old Bony stopped, his head drooping, weary enough at the day's end. The boys jumped down from the wagon and began to unload the wild hay, stacking it upon a pile already begun.

It was nearly dark when they finished. They went to the small stream that ran past the cabin, washed their faces and hands and went hungrily in for their supper.

The rest of the family had already gathered in the one big room that served as living room, dining room, kitchen and bedroom for the family. Brigham went straight to the big bed in one corner, where his lovely, pale mother lay under a patchwork quilt.

"Hello, Ma!"

"Hello, son. How did things go today?"

"All right. We finished cutting the wild hay down by the creek. Got quite a stack now, Ma. Should do for a good part of the winter."

"You're good boys. Eat your supper now. Fanny has it ready."

Brigham went across the room to the long table with its wooden benches and stools around it. Fanny, the oldest sister at home, was busy at the fireplace, where a huge iron kettle was bubbling. The boy watched his sister as she dished up the fragrant stew, raked potatoes out of the coals and broke off chunks of hot corn bread for each one. She looked much like his mother, except that she was young and strong, while his mother was pale and weak. Fanny was a grown woman. She was keeping company with one of the boys in Sherburne. Whenever Brigham thought of this young man his heart felt heavy. He didn't know what they'd do if Fanny got married.

Rhoda, almost as grown-up as Fanny, helped dish up the dinner, her brown eyes merry and her tongue ready with a quick saying. Nabby, fifteen, took a wooden bowl and a spoon and sat beside her mother's bed, helping the invalid eat. Susanna set the small Louisa on a stool and tied a bib in front of her chin. Louisa was the baby now, but she wouldn't be for long, Brigham knew.

The girls were all plenty busy, Brigham thought, grinning to himself. Well, the boys had had their turn at work, and they could do the girls' work, too, if they had to. They all knew how to wash dishes and churn and redd up the house. Joseph and Phineas already had their filled bowls before them, as did their father, at the end of the table. Only Nancy and John, the eldest boy, were absent. Nancy was married and living in a cabin of her own and John was apprenticed out to learn a trade.

When the last bowl was on the table and the last child seated, their father looked at them and smiled. He was a stern man, but a loving one. He expected piety and obedience among his children, but he could also sing a stirring song and tell an exciting story, particularly about the great war, where he had served in four engagements under the great General Washington himself—or about his long walk home when the war was over, a hundred miles or more, carrying a cannon ball all the way. That cannon ball was right in the room with them now. Brigham's eyes sought the familiar souvenir as they did so often when his father was talking.

Now his father spoke. "Let us bow our heads and give thanks to the Lord for what He this day has given us."

The cheery bustle in the room was hushed. The children bowed their heads and their father's voice rang out, solemn and reverent, as he gave thanks for their blessings.

After supper, Father Young took the big Bible from its shelf, while the children sat around him and listened to the reading of the evening verse. Then the boys went outside to sleep, for the yard was their bedroom during the summer months, the stars their candlelight.

When Brigham opened his eyes the next morning he lay still for a few moments, looking up into the clear sky above him. Then he felt Phineas stir beside him and he said, "It's a good day, Phin, a good day for that preacher man."

Then they were up, scrubbing themselves in the cold water of the stream, putting on their washed and faded Sunday jeans and hickory shirts, slicking down their unruly locks. When they went in to breakfast they were neat and clean for the Lord's day.

"Morning, Pa! Morning, Ma!"

Breakfast on the Sabbath day was a simple affair, as the Youngs did no work that could be avoided. Fanny came in from the barnyard, the milk pails brimming. She strained the milk into crocks and Rhoda poured it, still warm and foamy, into mugs for the children. With chunks of yesterday's bread, this was their breakfast.

Then Father Young brought up Old Bony, hitched again to the rickety wagon. Joseph toted out a big rocking chair and placed it carefully in the wagon bed, with chunks of wood under the rockers to hold it firmly in place. Brigham stood watching by the doorway as his father carried out the quilt-wrapped bundle that was Ma, and set it gently in the rocker. Pa would never drop her, Brigham knew, but he couldn't help holding his breath, just the same.

The boys snatched up their straw hats. They were homemade, each boy having woven his own. Their father was an expert basketmaker, but he had little time to spend on weaving hats for his children. They all climbed into the wagon; Pa picked up the lines, clucked to Old Bony, and they set off.

"Ma's awful white this morning," Brigham whispered to Susanna. "I hope she don't get sick at the meeting."

"She won't," Susanna said stoutly. "You're a scaredy, Brig Young. Pa'll take care of her."

"I wish she'd stay home. I'd stay and take care of her," Brigham persisted, trouble in his blue eyes. "I don't care whether I hear that preacher or not."

"Ma cares. She wouldn't miss meeting for anything. She can't sing in the choir while she's sick, but she loves the singing. And she loves to hear the preacher."

"What's his name, anyway? I heard it, but I don't remember—"

"Lorenzo Dow, that's what it is. He's a great man, Pa says—greatest preacher he ever heard. Ma says so, too. She says if the new baby's a boy she's going to name it Lorenzo Dow after the preacher."

As the wagon moved along the rutted woodland road, Brigham saw other wagons like theirs, all going in the same direction. Most of the outfits weren't any better than theirs, but sometimes a spruce, well set up rig came dashing along. Then John Young would cluck to Bony, give the lines a pull and move out of the way to let the dashing outfit pass.

The camp meeting was to be held in a grove on the other side of Sherburne, and as the Youngs drove up they were greeted by neighbors and friends. They seemed to be favorites, and Brigham knew why. They were all good singers and their voices helped a lot in singing hymns at camp meetings.

"Hi, John! How're things with ye?" A neighbor would call out. Or, "Hello, Missus Young. How're you feelin' today? Gettin' any stronger? Just wait till the cool weather comes—that'll help a lot."

The wagon came to a stop and the children clambered down and went running toward the tent. They were stopped in their tracks by the stern voice of their father.

"Joseph! Phineas! Susanna!"

They turned, rebuked already by that tone.

"There'll be no running or playing on the Sabbath!"

"Yes, Pa!"

They moved along sedately, while their father tethered Old Bony, put a nose bag over his eager nose, then lifted his wife from her chair. Holding her tenderly, the big man carried her gently into the tent that had been set up in the grove. He placed her on a bench and sat beside her.

Everyone was there, Brigham thought, looking about him. He helped little Louisa onto the bench where the little girl crowded close to her mother's side.

"Don't be scared!" Brigham whispered. "Every time we come to meeting, you get scared."

The little girl stuffed her fist into her mouth and snuggled closer to her mother.

"Here, Briggy, move over. I'll sit by her," Nabby said.

Brigham slid along the plank seat. Before he knew what had happened, several people had crowded in between him and Nabby. He found himself right on the aisle, almost falling off the end of the rough plank that served for a bench. Brigham didn't like this. He knew that down this aisle would go the sinners—called to repentance by the preacher's wailing voice.

The first cry of the preacher startled him as it always did.

"Hallelujah!"

The crowd echoed the cry, roaring "Hallelujah! Hallelujah!"

Brigham slipped to his feet. He looked to the front of the tent and there was the preacher. He was a tall, dark, forbidding-looking man. A black beard almost covered his face. His mouth was red in the black forest of that beard. His long arms were outstretched, his head thrown back, his eyes staring upward. Then his voice rolled out, calling upon the sinners to repent.

Brigham didn't like it. He looked about and saw that no one was watching him. He began to edge down the aisle toward the door. His bare feet made no noise in the dust of the tent floor.

"Be saved before it is too late!" roared the preacher. Brigham slipped out of the hot, dusty tent, into the cool air of the grove.

It seemed as if no one else was outside. Everyone was listening to the preacher. But not quite everyone. Through the trees, the boy caught sight of a fluttering bit of crimson. Then his ears pricked up as he heard a strange, lilting sound—a sound he had never heard before. It seemed to be calling to him. Without actually meaning to, Brigham started through the trees toward the bit of color and the haunting music. And as he came nearer to the sound, he forgot his father's admonition against running on the Sabbath. His bare feet fairly flew over the leaf-strewn ground.

He stopped suddenly. There, in a small clearing, sat a man. And under his chin was tucked a shining piece of wood, over which his hands and fingers fluttered mysteriously. It was this that made the music, Brigham saw at once, even before he noticed that the man was old and dark skinned, his straggly black hair tied back with a crimson scarf.

The old man saw Brigham and he smiled. Then, with the music still ringing so hauntingly, he said, "You like, yes?"

Brigham couldn't answer. This was a gypsy, he knew now, and no one spoke to gypsies. But he couldn't tear himself away from that music. His feet began to beat time. The tune changed from its sweet, beseeching tone to something gay and happy. Brigham's feet were almost dancing to keep up with the merry sound.

Suddenly a heavy hand smacked him soundly, and Brigham almost lost his balance. He turned, startled, to see his father's frowning face above him.

"Thou shalt not desecrate the Sabbath!" his father said sternly. "This is not the day to be listening to the dancing jigs of a fiddle! The Devil's own music! Come back to the meeting and behave yourself as you have been taught to do. That's the Devil's music you're listening to—and I won't have it!"

Brigham blinked back the tears and followed his father through the trees. As they went, the music of the fiddle followed them.

"How can music like that be wrong?" he asked himself. "It sounds like heaven." He couldn't help listening to the music, which came more and more faintly to his straining ears. He dug his fist into his eyes.

"I don't believe the Devil has fiddles!" he muttered stubbornly. "I don't think there's music like that in hell."

CHAPTER TWO

THE FAMILY SCATTERS

->>->>->>->>->>->>-<<-<<-<<-<<-<<-<<-<<

"And the Lord went before them by day in a pillar of a cloud, to lead them the way; and by night in a pillar of fire to give them light; to go by day and night."

Father Young's rich voice paused and then went on, deep toned, "He took not away the pillar of the cloud by day, nor the pillar of fire by night, from before the people."

Slowly he closed the big Bible on his knees. He lifted his eyes and looked about him. Beside him in her rocking chair sat his wife. Around them were grouped the children, entranced by the story. From the oldest to the youngest, no one moved or spoke for a moment. Then Brigham sighed.

"That's my very favorite story in the Bible. Moses leading the Children of Israel!" he whispered to Susanna.

The spell was broken. The children began to stretch and talk.

Their mother spoke softly. "Let's sing a hymn before we go to bed. Now we are all together again. Tomorrow night John will be gone away to his work. It is so good to have him here. I feel to sing—"

John smiled at his mother. He was a well-built fellow of twenty-one, but he felt small and helpless when he looked at his pale mother. There was nothing he could do to relieve her continuous suffering.

Without waiting for suggestions, Father Young's deep baritone began:

18

"Praise ye the Lord!
Timbrel and harp employ;
Lift the voice; sing, rejoice,
Publish His greatness and glory!"

They all joined in, singing with enthusiasm and reverence. As they finished the hymn, little Lorenzo Dow dug his chubby fist into his eyes, yawning and snuffling sleepily.

Eight-year-old Louisa wiped his nose and cuddled him. "Time for bed, Renny!" she said tenderly.

The older girls began to bustle about, doing the little before-bed chores. The boys sat still around their parents.

"I was pleased with your preaching yesterday, John," Father Young commented quietly. "You were a bit diffident, but you'll get over that. It was a good meeting, wasn't it? So many sinners confessing."

John's face flushed with pleasure at his father's praise. "I listen to every preacher that comes along," he admitted, "and try to learn something from each one. But of course Preacher Dow is my model—"

In spite of himself, an impish grin twisted Brigham's lips. "You can't ever yell like he does! You ain't got the voice *nor* looks!"

. . . . ," his father said
. . . his words c . . .
. . . k like this, Ph . . . igham insisted.
. . . thing I don't . . . the boy.
. . . do other bad thing . . . can't get the
. . . told us that—and Ma. . . . d the Bible
. . . o read the Bible and . . . e church."
. . . at's all Preacher Dow . . . e's got his
. . . e bad. I don't think . . . m. Now I,"
. . . . I've come

. . . hat do you want a . . . ," his mother
. . . you those things. I

said softly. "He'll see the light one of these days. I know
he's searching earnestly."

"I want to be a preacher, Pa, full time," John said. "Travel
all over the country preaching. Nothing else seems to suit
me. What do you think, Pa?"

Father Young's eyes glistened. "I'd like for one of my sons
to be a preacher. I'd have liked that myself. To carry the
word of God to unbelievers! It is the best work a man can
engage in."

"Well, leave Brig to me, then. I'll bring him into the fold."

As Brigham lay beside Phineas a little later that night, he
asked, "Tell me, Phin, how did you feel—inside—when you
were confirmed?"

"I felt good—all excited and alive—like I was washed
clean—"

Brigham sat up in bed. His blue eyes probed the darkness
to the pale oval that was his brother's face.

"Washed clean—just by *saying* something? It don't make
sense to me, Phin. I don't know why, but it just don't!"

"Don't you listen to what Preacher Dow yells at you?
Repent and be saved! Come to the Lord! Don't that scare
you some?"

Brigham shook his head. "No, it don't scare me
think like this—" He stopped to choose
to match his difficult thought. "I thin
Preacher Dow don't tell me a single
know. He says not to lie and steal an
But we know that already, Phin. Pa's
Ma ain't no preacher but she tells us
to keep away from bad things. And th
says—and that we're bad—all of us a
so—"

"Well, for goodness sakes, Brig, w
preacher to do? That's his job—to tel

guess there's lots of mothers, maybe, don't tell their children the things Ma tells us, and the preacher has to do it."

Brigham's eyes were troubled. "But we know that already," he repeated stubbornly. "What I want a preacher to do is to tell me about God—what's He like; what He thinks—"

"You're crazy as a loon, Brig Young!" Phineas snorted. "Nobody knows those things. Nobody. Now be still and go to sleep or you won't be awake in time to tell John good-by tomorrow morning."

Phineas turned his back and flung one arm up over his head so he wouldn't be able to hear any more of his brother's foolish talk.

Brigham slid down under the coverlet and stopped talking. But he didn't stop thinking.

Why didn't the preachers know all about God? Why couldn't they tell him what God looked like and what heaven was like, what he was like before he was born and he'd be like after he died? Why did the preachers keep saying people were sinners? If only someone would answer his questions!

He frowned, puzzled, as he remembered how he had gone up to the famous Preacher Dow and had asked respectfully, "Preacher Dow, will you tell me something?"

The great man had looked down at the boy and put a big hand on his head.

"Certainly! Certainly, my lad! What is it?"

But when Brigham had phrased his question the preacher had just stared down at him for a long time. Then he had boomed, "You're too young to understand those things now. Wait a bit, my lad. Wait a bit!"

Lying in the dark, remembering, Brigham felt baffled resentment.

"He didn't know the answer!" he told himself. "He didn't know."

Still puzzling over the many questions that troubled him, Brigham fell asleep at last.

Three years later, Brigham was still asking questions, still seeking answers that he seldom received. And suddenly he wanted desperately to know.

He was standing in the big kitchen, watching his father turn the leaves of the much-used Bible. The room seemed empty and still. Over in the corner, the patchwork coverlet lay smooth and flat upon the bed. Brigham could not look that way. His mother, who had lain there so patiently year after year, was gone now. She never again would say, "Hello, son. How did the day go?"

Brigham ran his fingers through his softly curling hair. He swallowed and asked, "Will we see her again, Pa?"

"If we are worthy, son. At the Resurrection—"

"Will she remember us, Pa?"

His father spoke gently. "You'd better come into the church, Brigham. There's comfort in religion."

"I will, Pa, maybe, someday."

"Brigham, we must think what to do. The girls, Fanny and Nancy, will take the smaller children. And they want me to live with them. I thought I'd go to Fanny for a while. But we can't expect them to take us all—"

"I know, Pa. I've thought about it. Thought maybe I could get apprenticed out."

Looking at the boy, the father's face softened. "I might have known you'd think of it, son. You're a good boy, church or no church. What do you aim to do?"

"I like to make things—with wood, especially. I thought maybe Hy Waggoner could take me into his shop—teach me to be a carpenter."

"That's fine. I'll talk to Hy tonight. I'm pretty sure he'll be glad to have you. He's been saying he needs help. Phineas and Joseph will go to Tom Barker's farm for a while. They both want to be preachers like John—when they can get to it."

Brigham went close to his father. "I listen to John when he preaches. He sounds so sure, Pa. But I just can't be sure—"

His father sighed. "It would bring you comfort, son. Remember that. You're going to be lonely for a while, with us scattered about. But we're still a family, son. Remember that, too. We won't be too far away, no matter where you go. And if you want us, we'll be waiting to help you." He laid his hand on Brigham's head. "Keep in close touch with us, son. Keep in close touch."

Brigham felt tears burn along the edge of his eyelids. "I will, Pa!" he promised.

CHAPTER THREE

A BOOK AND A PROMISE

>>>->>>->>>->>>->>>->>>->>>->>>->>>

"Giddy-up, horsey! giddy-up!"

Four-year-old Elizabeth kicked her heels against her father's shoulders. Her chubby fingers were clutching his thick, curly hair.

"Giddy-up! Giddy-up!"

Brigham Young, his little daughter astride his broad shoulders, galloped about the room. He tossed his head and neighed.

"Whoa, horsey! Whoa!" Elizabeth yanked at her father's hair, pulling back, as she had seen him pull on the lines to stop a team.

Brigham whinnied, reared back and pretended he was trying to buck the small rider off.

From her rocking chair by the window his wife watched them. Her clear laugh rippled out.

"Oh, Brigham, you're such a boy!"

Brigham set the little girl down on the floor and went to Miriam.

"Boy?" he asked chuckling. "Didn't you hear my knees creak? An old man of twenty-nine and you call me boy!"

Miriam laughed again. She lifted her white hand and ran her fingers through her husband's soft, light hair.

"Yes, boy!" she repeated tenderly. "And your knees will never creak, Brigham. You keep them too well limbered up."

Elizabeth climbed up onto her mother's lap. Brigham's arms went around both of them.

They were sitting thus when the door burst open and Phineas came in. There was an air of excitement about him.

"Hello, Phin!" Brigham exclaimed, going to greet his brother. "What are you doing here in Mendon?"

"How's your father?" Miriam asked, "and the rest of the family?"

"They're all well." Phineas couldn't keep the feverish animation out of his voice. "Brigham, we've found something—something that should interest you."

He held out a small tan book. Brigham took it and turned it over in his strong, firm fingers.

"Book of Mormon," he read. "What is it, Phineas?"

"It's a new scripture—a book that gives the gospel of salvation. It has been translated by revelation from golden plates, to restore the old, true religion. It teaches the ancient principles, as Jesus taught them—repentance, salvation through baptism—"

"Hold on a minute!" Brigham laid a hand on his brother's shoulder. "You're running away with yourself. How do you know all this?"

"I've read the book and my mind has been opened to receive it," Phineas answered soberly.

"But Book of Mormon!" Brigham insisted. "I don't under-stand—"

"Part of the original record—not this translation, but the original, on golden plates—was written by Mormon. He was a prophet of olden times here on this continent. Part was written by others, but Mormon gave the whole record its name. The new church—or rather the ancient church restored—is called the Church of Jesus Christ of Latter-day Saints. When you read the book, Brigham, you'll recognize that it must be true. It restores all the ancient orders—elders, teachers, apostles, deacons. And all the ancient rites—

baptism by immersion, the sacrament. Read it, that's all I ask. I hurried to bring it to you to share my discovery."

A wry smile twisted Brigham's lips. "Phineas! Phineas!" he exclaimed gently. "You preached at me and badgered me until I joined the Methodists, and then, before I get a fair start there, you come rushing in with a new religion. That's what held me back for so many years. No one is sure—"

"I'm sure now. Truly sure for the first time," Phineas said firmly.

Miriam came and stood beside the two men, little Elizabeth clinging to her skirt.

"Let me see the book," she said. She took the small tan volume and opened it at random. Then she began to read.

"Sit down, Phineas, and tell us about this," Brigham said.

Phineas sat down on a sturdy stool, the handiwork he knew, of Brigham. In his eagerness he leaned forward.

"It was this way. A man named Samuel Smith was selling these books in Livonia. He came to Fanny's house and asked for the Reverend John P. Greene. Fanny told him that that was her husband, but he wasn't home just then."

Brigham's lips quirked in his humorous smile. "He was trying to sell this new Bible to a Methodist minister?"

"He was trying to sell it to everybody. John came in just then and listened to the man. You know how courteous John is. He said if the fellow would leave the book, he'd study it and decide whether they wanted it."

Brigham nodded, his eyes twinkling. "That's John!"

"Well, Fanny and John looked it over and decided not to buy it. But when Smith came back and they told him this, he looked at them in a strange way and said, 'Keep it, anyway, friends. Pray God to help you see the light!' And he went away."

Miriam sighed. "He must have been a strange man!"

"His way was a bit strange, Fanny thought. But they took the book and studied it more carefully, compared it with

the Bible, prayed—and suddenly they knew it was the truth—
every word of it."

"But what is in it?" Brigham insisted. He took the book
from his wife's hands and studied it curiously.

"Much more than I can tell you now, Brigham. It's the
record of some families that escaped from Jerusalem long
before the time of Christ. They came to this continent and
brought with them certain records—records engraved on
plates of brass. They preserved these from generation to
generation. Finally one, Mormon, condensed them all and
engraved them on plates of gold."

"Where are they now, these people? Or their descendants?"

"They're still here, some of them. Most were killed in
wars between the tribes, but some survived—the Lamanites—
Indians—"

Brigham leaned forward, suddenly attentive. "You mean
it tells where the Indians came from? How they got their
red skins? I've wondered about that."

Phineas nodded. "And much more. After Mormon made
his abridgment of the records, he died. And his son Moroni
hid the golden plates in the hill of Cumorah, over in Wayne
County, near Palmyra. Of course this was hundreds of years
ago, and no one knew they were there till the Angel Moroni
came to the Prophet and told him—"

"What prophet?"

"Joseph Smith—the Prophet and the head of this new
church. The Lord has spoken to him and has sent angels to
him—"

"A prophet? A living prophet today? He heard God's
voice—" Brigham's eyes were shining with a strange light.
"You know, Phineas, I have tried all the religions—listened
to them."

Phineas nodded and Brigham went on, "I saw folks getting
religion all around me and I tried to get the feeling of it. I

tried them all, but not one of them had any effect on me. But you know, if I could see the face of a prophet, such as lived on earth in the olden days, if I could meet up with a man to whom the heavens were opened and who knew God and His character, and what God is and where He is—I'd crawl on my hands and knees to find him. I would give up everything I own and serve him, through all my life."

He spoke so earnestly and his voice had such a ring of sincerity that Phineas and Miriam both looked at him in wonder. Even little Elizabeth stared up at her father, her eyes wide with awe.

Brigham was silent for a moment and then he went on more quietly, "That's the way I feel about it, Phineas. But I'm not going to jump to the conclusion that this book will lead me where I want to go. I'll take it and study it, as I've studied everything that came my way since our mother taught me how to read. But I'm not going to jump at any conclusions."

"You'll find it's true," Phineas said positively. "Come to Livonia with me and talk to Pa and John."

Brigham shook his head firmly. "No. What they say would not make any difference, any more than it has in the past. I've got to decide for myself."

For two long years Brigham studied the little tan volume, but there was not much time he could spare from his work as a carpenter and glazier. Another daughter had been born to them. They had named her Vilate, in honor of the wife of Brigham's best friend Heber Kimball. But Miriam, always sickly, did not recover fully after her second child's birth, and the burden of keeping up the house and caring for his wife and two children fell entirely on Brigham's shoulders.

Of course he had shown the book to Heber, and the two spent many winter evenings reading and discussing its contents.

The teachings appealed strongly to the two earnest young

men. They liked the idea that man is immortal and that this life is just a stage in an eternal march of progression. They liked to think that at an appointed time they would rise from the dead with their own bodies and would then be reunited with family and friends, just as in this world, only better.

Brigham, particularly, was pleased with the teaching that everyone would go on working in this perfect life. To him, the thought of an eternity of idleness, or harp-playing, was obnoxious. And he liked the thought that all men might be saved—all of them. He believed that God was kind and just; and that if a man did his part faithfully, he could trust God to stand beside him. And this new religion taught that, too.

Now, in the early spring of 1832, he had come to his decision.

As he moved deftly about the big room, getting breakfast for the family, he was thinking how much like his own childhood home this home was. And he gave silent thanks that he had been taught as a boy how to do all the necessary household chores.

When the corn meal mush was bubbling in the iron kettle, Brigham went to the trundle bed where Elizabeth lay, patiently waiting for permission to get up.

"Up, Lizzie!" her father called cheerfully. "Up, my big girl, and get dressed. Such a clever girl she is, and such a help to her pa."

While Elizabeth struggled with her clothing, Brigham lifted the baby from beside her mother. He carried her across the room to his own sturdy chair. Holding her on his lap, he took off her nightdress and put on her day clothes.

He set the little girls at the table, its pine top white from frequent scrubbings, and placed bowls of mush before them. Then he went to Miriam.

"It's a beautiful morning, Miriam!" he said smiling. "From

your window today, you can actually see the grass sprouting and the dandelions popping out of the ground."

Miriam's thin hand brushed her husband's cheek. "You are so good to us, Brigham."

"I feel good." As he gently washed his wife's face and hands and brushed her long, soft hair, he went on. "Miriam," he said, "I have reached a decision. I am going to be baptized into this new church of Jesus Christ of Latter-day Saints, the Mormons, as people are calling them now, because they have this Book of Mormon. I have made up my mind—and I have never before known such peace."

Miriam's eyes lighted with happiness. "I'm glad, Brigham, for your sake."

His strong arm went around her thin shoulders and he held her close to his heart. With his lips against her hair he whispered, "It promises me something, Miriam! I shall never lose you—we'll be together as long as we both live, and then on, after we die—through all eternity. You and I and our children, Miriam, always together."

Miriam closed her eyes to hide the sudden pain that dimmed them. She was sure she had a very short time left to be with her husband here in this life. She had dreaded leaving him, as his mother had left him, alone and lonely. But this promise of an eternal life together, that made it easier to bear, both for him and for her.

Brigham wrapped Miriam in a warm robe and carried her to the rocking chair by the window.

"Vilate Kimball will look in from time to time as usual," he said. "And if you need me for anything, Lizzie can run down to the shop for me."

He kissed them all and left, turning at the gate to wave at the pale face watching from the window.

It was a perfect spring day, that day of April 24, 1832, when Brigham went down into the water of Mendon Creek to be baptized by Elder Miller. A strange exaltation filled him. This is what I have waited for, he thought. No doubts. No fears. I am into this church body and soul, as I am in this water. And his heart seemed to beat out "Hosanna!"

As he emerged from the stream, dripping, Elder Miller laid his hands on Brigham's head and ordained him an elder in the church.

The next day Heber Kimball was baptized, and before long Brigham's brothers and sisters and his wife had followed his example.

It was not too soon for Miriam. In September she died and Brigham, bereft and lonely, turned passionately to the work of his new religion.

CHAPTER FOUR

INTRODUCTION TO LEADERSHIP

≫≫≫≫≫≫≫≫≫≫≫

Brigham looked up from the chair he was making. Heber Kimball stood in the doorway of the tiny shop. His hair was ruffled by the autumn wind. His good-natured face was excited and his merry eyes serious.

"What's this your brother Joseph tells me? You're going to Ohio?"

Brigham nodded. "That's right, Heber. I've made up my mind to go to Kirtland and see for myself. Here it's been five months since I was baptized. I've been traveling about over the countryside, preaching and baptizing. But I have never seen the one man—the Prophet—"

"But your work—your shop—"

Brigham shrugged, "A man's real work is to serve God."

The two friends looked deep into each other's eyes. They were almost exactly the same age, Heber just two weeks younger than Brigham. But they were of widely different natures. Brigham was rather serious, very practical and down to earth. His humor was the gentle kind that saw the irony of a situation, the drollery of human nature. He could be brusque and stern when necessary, playful with children, thoughtful of women, but generally he was quietly plain spoken. Heber, on the other hand, was a merry soul. He liked practical jokes, funny stories, rollicking parties.

After Miriam's death, the Kimballs had taken the Youngs into their home. Vilate Kimball had cared for the two little girls as if they were her own. Brigham had been more than welcome upon his return from the various missionary journeys he had taken. One of the main teachings of his new-found religion was that the message of salvation should be carried to all peoples. The Indians—Lamanites—were particularly important, and Brigham had accepted his share of this work, knowing how well his little girls would be cared for in his absence.

Now Heber said, "I'm glad you've made this decision, Brigham. I'll go with you, of course. And Joseph wants to make the trip, he says."

"I think we should start at once, so we can get back before snowfall."

Heber chuckled. "Snowfall shouldn't scare you, Brigham, especially after that trip we made by sleigh last winter down into Pennsylvania. I'll have my carriage ready. We can start tomorrow."

Brigham's blue eyes regarded his friend. There was a look of deep affection in them, for Brigham knew that the offer of the carriage and the companionship would make his journey to Kirtland, Ohio, much easier.

And it was to Kirtland they planned to go, for there Joseph Smith, founder of the new church, had taken up his home and made the church headquarters.

That carriage trip from Mendon to Kirtland, nearly three hundred miles, in the fall of the year was a beautiful excursion. Down around the southern shores of Lake Ontario and Lake Erie the three good friends made their way. At night they stopped with Mormon families, for the missionaries of the new religion had traversed all this country and had made a number of converts.

It was early afternoon when Heber drew his horse to a stop in front of the cabin of John P. Greene, Brigham's brother-in-law, who had moved to Kirtland as Joseph Smith had urged all converts to do. The three travelers wasted little time in exchanging bits of news with their host. They asked to be shown where Joseph lived, then set out at once for the house pointed out to them.

Brigham knocked at the door and a tall, dark woman opened it. Her hair was parted severely in the center and drawn back straight behind the ears. She was dressed simply in a dark, full dress, with a small shawl around her shoulders. Her black eyes regarded Brigham with friendly interest.

"Does the Prophet Joseph live here?" Brigham asked.

"Yes. I am Emma Smith, his wife. Joseph is cutting wood out yonder in the grove. You may come in and wait for him, if you wish."

Brigham shook his head. "We've come a long way to see him. We'd like to find him at once, if that is possible."

"Yes. You'll find him down there." She nodded toward a thick growth of trees a short distance away.

"Thank you, ma'am," Brigham replaced the broad-brimmed hat he had borrowed for the trip. Nearly all his clothing had been borrowed by him or given to him for this journey. Back in Mendon, he had given away all his possessions, in order to be utterly free to travel and to do whatever he might be called upon to do for the church.

He turned to his companions, a puzzled frown on his brow.

"I suppose we'll have to go down to the grove. The Prophet is out there cutting wood." The statement must have sounded just a bit strange, for Brigham's voice was somewhat troubled.

Heber was astonished. "It can't be!" he exclaimed. "Cutting wood? The Prophet? He should not be doing that kind of work!"

Brigham's brow cleared and he smiled his sudden, winning smile. "Well, I don't know about that, Heber. Cutting wood might be the Lord's work as much as anything else, seems to me. But we'll see. We'll see."

Heber nodded, reassured. He knew that Brigham had an

uncanny faculty for judging people. His estimation of a man was seldom wrong. If he saw Joseph Smith, spoke to him and declared him to be a true prophet, Heber would never question his judgment.

The three men made their way swiftly down to the grove. In a compact little group they moved through the trees toward the sound of axes ringing against wood. As they came into a small clearing they saw three men energetically swinging axes.

One was a tall man, well over six feet. He was strongly built and possessed broad shoulders. He swung his arms with power and rhythm. He wore a white shirt with long, full sleeves, rather incongruous for the sort of works he was doing. The sunlight, coming in little patches through the leaves, struck his light brown hair and seemed to set him apart with warm radiance. Without a moment's hesitation, Brigham approached him.

The ax stopped in the middle of a stroke, and the tall man turned to his visitor. Brigham's quick eyes studied the person before him. He saw a well-shaped head covered by thick, wavy hair brushed back from a high forehead. The face was handsome, with a large aquiline nose which would have completely dominated another face, but here was subdued by the prominence and fire of the fine blue eyes. Heavy eyelids, fringed with long, dark lashes, gave to these eyes a look of mystery and dreaminess.

"You are the Prophet Joseph!" Brigham exclaimed. "We have come from the Saints in Monroe County, New York, to visit you. I am Brigham Young."

The ax dropped and a strong, shapely hand came out to grasp Brigham's. "I am glad to see you, Brother Brigham. We need Saints in Kirtland to help build up the kingdom."

Brigham introduced his companions and they all shook hands.

"Come to the house," Joseph invited. "We'll have a talk."

He buried the ax blade in a stump, and without more ado led the newcomers back to his cottage.

When they entered, Brigham looked around curiously. It was as simply furnished as any frontier cabin—stark wooden chairs, plain pine table, a stone fireplace, homemade rag rugs on the floor. Brigham liked this. To him it spoke of simplicity and honesty.

There were two women in the cabin. One Brigham had already met. The other was an old woman. She sat in a rocking chair, her hands busy with knitting.

Joseph indicated the two with a courteous nod toward each. "Emma, my wife, and Lucy Smith, my mother."

It seemed natural for Brigham to assume the role of spokesman for the trio. He was younger than his brother Joseph, but more fluent with words. And Heber Kimball was an extremely shy man, in spite of his merry nature. So Brigham reported briefly on the work and the Saints around Mendon. Then he listened attentively while Joseph reviewed the organization of the Church of Jesus Christ of Latter-day Saints on April 6, 1830, at Fayette, New York.

"Only two and a half years ago there were only six of us at that organization," Joseph said proudly. "Now we are hundreds!"

Brigham listened enthralled to the ardent voice. Here was a man who, like himself, had been born and reared on a small farm. Here was no great scholar, no product of universities or schools of theology. Here was no ranting and yelling as Brigham had heard so often from revivalist preachers. The man spoke simply and plainly, yet with complete assurance and authority. And he spoke of God as if he knew Him.

There was no need for Joseph to explain the beliefs of the church. Brigham had mentioned that he had studied the Book of Mormon for two years before accepting baptism. Brigham knew the principles well. But he did want to hear from Joseph's own lips about the troubles that had driven the Saints from New York to Ohio.

Joseph explained briefly. "My neighbors could not believe in modern day revelation," he said. "They objected to baptism by immersion. The things God had instructed me to do brought anger and mobbing upon us. And so we moved west, here to Kirtland, where our missionaries had already had marvelous success in teaching the gospel."

Late in the afternoon the group walked out to look over the new city. Here Joseph was planning to build a model community. He pointed out the hill he had chosen as the site for the temple, where the sacred rites of the church could be performed. As they walked along the neat, well-kept streets, Brigham marveled at what the Saints had done within the two years they had been located here.

When evening came, a number of the leading men gathered at Joseph's cottage to meet the New York Saints. Among them were Joseph's father and his brother Hyrum. The little group opened its meeting by singing a hymn. It was sung to an old tune, one Brigham knew well. But the words were new and strange.

> "The Lord hath brought again Zion;
> The Lord hath redeemed his people, Israel;
> Glory and honor and power and might
> Be ascribed to our God forever and ever, Amen!"

As the voices rang out triumphantly on the last line, Brigham turned to the man sitting next to him.

"That is a new hymn. I have never heard it before."

"It was revealed to Joseph, for our use. The old hymns will not do for the new church."

Israel! Brigham thought. Zion! Yes, the new church was founded on the records of Israel. And like Israel, it was surrounded by unbelievers. He remembered his father's rich voice reading the story of Moses as his children sat about him.

Now Joseph, paying honor to his guest, asked Brigham to pray. Still caught in the exaltation of the hymn, Brigham knelt, bowed his head and began to speak. But the words that came were in a tongue strange to his listeners. They knelt around him, spellbound. When the flow of strange syllables ceased, Brigham shook his head as if awakening from a dream, then rose, trembling. The others looked from him to Joseph.

"What does this mean?" they asked.

Joseph smiled gently. "He spoke in the pure Adamic tongue."

"You mean the language used by Adam and Eve?" they asked incredulously.

"Even so," Joseph answered.

"But where did he learn it?"

Heber Kimball spoke up. "He didn't learn it. Ever since his baptism, Brother Brigham has had this strange power. It comes upon him suddenly, when he is transported. Then he speaks as you heard."

Joseph Young put in a word. "Sometimes no one can tell what he has said. At other times, someone in the congregation is given divine power to comprehend and translate Brother Brigham's words."

"But isn't it wrong?" they persisted. For Joseph had frowned upon the emotional exhibitions of revivalists.

"No," their leader answered serenely. "It is of God." His voice took on a prophetic tone as he said softly to Heber Kimball, "Someday this man will preside over the entire church!"

That night as Brigham lay beside Heber at John Greene's cabin, he said softly, "You were right, Heber. The Prophet should not be out cutting wood. His is the voice that speaks eternal truths. Others should provide the hands and feet to do the physical work of the church."

"There are plenty of others here," Heber agreed, "to say nothing of the Saints in New York, Pennsylvania, Missouri and other places—wherever the missionaries have carried the good work forward."

"Yes, there are plenty. But I am afraid many of them are not willing to give up their own aims and purposes to serve with a whole heart and an undivided interest. But I am eager to do just that, Heber. I will give everything I own— all my days and all my thoughts—to building up the kingdom of God upon this earth."

"And I am right beside you, Brigham!" Heber said with fervor.

A few days later the trio from Mendon turned homeward again. They had been asked by Joseph to go back and bring their families down to Kirtland. One of the first principles of the new religion was a concept known as "gathering." Saints from all the corners of the earth should gather together to build up Zion. And Kirtland was the first gathering place chosen for this purpose.

Sine it was too late in the season to make the move that year, Brigham put in those winter months preaching in and around Kingston, Canada. He traveled many, many miles on foot, poorly clothed, through snow and ice and bitter winds to carry his message to others. Often, as he trudged along lonely, unmarked paths, his ragged shoes were filled with blood from his torn and lacerated feet. His shabby coat could not keep out the fierce winter blasts. But Brigham did not complain. He had a job to do, and he went about it filled with high enthusiasm.

Early in the summer of 1833, he sold out what property he had in Mendon. By September he and his little group of friends and relatives were ready to move to Kirtland.

It was only a small party. Many of the men were older

than Brigham. Yet from the very first, without ostentation or presumption, Brigham was unquestionably the leader. It was to him they came for advice on what to sell and what to keep, what kind of vehicles to use, what provisions to carry.

And when the little caravan formed, it was Heber's carriage with Brigham Young and his family in it that led the way.

CHAPTER FIVE

TROUBLE IN OHIO

➤➤➤-➤➤➤-➤➤➤-➤➤➤-➤➤➤-➤➤➤-➤➤➤-➤➤➤-➤➤➤

When Brigham brought his little group of New York converts to Kirtland, he found they were only one of dozens of such parties pouring into the new community from all parts of the East and North. Every day brought wagons loaded with families and possessions. The families were settled wherever they could find someone to take them in.

A good part of each newcomer's possessions was turned over to the church, for at this time the Saints were living a modified communal life. Each man gave whatever he could spare to the common storehouse, and each donated his own labor to help the newcomers and the church. "From each according to his gifts and to each according to his needs," was the motto.

Brigham lived this principle to the full. He turned over to the church all that he had received for his property in Mendon. He set out with nothing of his own to help build up the new Zion. His skill as a carpenter, painter and glazier was in constant demand. There was the temple to build, and a schoolhouse, as well as homes for the many newcomers. He worked fast, efficiently and tirelessly. It came to be the common thing to "call on Brother Brigham." And Brother Brigham always responded.

Besides this physical work for the church and its people, for which Brigham expected and received no pay, he had his spiritual work to do. He was meticulous about attending all church services and all special meetings to which Joseph

Smith called him. And he even found time to go out into the surrounding country, as far away as the eastern seaboard, preaching the gospel and winning converts to the new religion. In these travels he carried no money with him, as his church forbade the elders and the missionaries to receive pay. He trusted solely upon his persuasiveness to find food and lodging wherever he went.

Yet in spite of all these demands upon his time and energy, Brigham managed to find himself a wife and to build her a home. His wife was Mary Ann Angel, an intelligent, very religious woman. She had made herself a promise that she would never marry until she found a "man of God," and in the earnestly devout Brigham Young she found the person that satisfied this requirement.

They were married in February of 1834. Mary Ann took the two little daughters of Brigham straight to her heart, and once again Brigham had a home of his own and his family all together. It seem to give him even more enthusiasm and energy for his church work. With Mary Ann's unwavering support—for no matter what the church asked Brigham to do, Mary Ann approved—he accomplished prodigious labors among the people.

Not long after Brigham's marriage, Joseph Smith organized Zion's Camp. This was an "army" of two hundred and fifty carefully chosen men, who were to march to Missouri to help their fellow Saints who were having trouble in that state. Brigham, of course, was one of the selected men.

About three years before, Joseph Smith had gone to Missouri to look over the missionary work being done there. For, with their zeal for winning souls, Mormon missionaries had been sent to the frontier of civilization—the settlements in Missouri. There Joseph had met his associates at Independence, in Jackson County. It was beautiful country and the young Mormon leader felt that this was the place for the new Zion. As fast as he could he would have all the

Saints gather here. Accordingly, hundreds of families from
New York, Pennsylvania and Ohio had already moved to
Independence and its neighboring area.

And they were having serious troubles now with the old
settlers. There were many reasons for these troubles. The
Mormons were mainly Yankees; they did not believe in
slavery; they spoke with a different accent from the soft,
slow drawl of the southerners. The Mormons were also dis-
concertingly energetic and thrifty. Their neat, prosperous
farms put their neighbors' unkempt patches to shame. But
worst of all, in the eyes of the Missourians, was the fact that
the Saints thought of this land as their own. Here they were
going to build their Zion. All these choice lands would
someday belong to them.

And so trouble began. Mobs of Missourians formed. They
decided they must drive the Mormons out before Zion could
be built, but the Mormons didn't take to the idea of leaving.
They had bought the lands they owned and they wanted
to keep them. The Missouri folk became more and more
angry and scared. They began to burn the houses and hay-
stacks and the standing crops of the Saints. They drove
away cattle and even threw stones at the Mormons when
they appeared on the streets.

The Saints sent word to Joseph telling him of their difficulties and asking for help. Joseph's answer was Zion's
Camp, which would march down to Missouri and settle the
trouble.

The men started out bravely, flags flying, band playing,
songs ringing out defiantly. Their favorite song was one
composed for this very event:

> "Hark, listen to the trumpeters!
> They sound for volunteers.
> On Zion's bright and flowery mount
> Behold the officers.

Their horses white, their armor bright,
With courage bold they stand,
Enlisting soldiers for their king
To march to Zion's land."

Brigham's voice rang out with the rest. With shoulders thrown back, his light hair lifted by the breeze, he marched along, confident and happy.

But Zion's Camp was destined to be of no help to their troubled comrades. Before the army reached Independence, cholera struck the camp. Many died; almost all were sick. Joseph ordered them back to Kirtland.

In Ohio, they took up the work they had left when they marched away, and foremost among their tasks was the building of the temple.

One cold February afternoon, Brigham and his brother Joseph were at the quarry getting out rock for the temple walls. Often Joseph Smith himself, as foreman of the building, would be working there side by side with his followers. Dressed in tow frock and pantaloons, his sleeves rolled up, his strength and energy set an example for the others.

But this day the leader was not at the quarry. He sent a messenger asking Brigham and his brother to come to the Smith home at once. The brothers laid aside their tools and hastened to obey the summons.

"I want you to notify all the brethern in the branches around here that we will hold a conference here next Saturday. I particularly want all the members of Zion's Camp to be here to receive a special blessing."

Brigham nodded thoughtfully. Those men who had unquestioningly marched two thousand miles deserved a special blessing.

"At that special conference," Joseph went on, "I shall complete the organization of the church. I shall appoint twelve special witnesses, or apostles, whose duty it shall be to open the door of the gospel to foreign nations. And you," his large eyes turned to Brigham, "you will be one of them."

When they left the leader's house, Brigham turned to his brother.

"I feel a great sense of happiness," he began. "But I scarcely believe I am worthy—"

"No one in the church is more worthy!" his brother said loyally. "No one has given more time, more service, than you. At any hour of the day or night, you have gone to help anyone who called on you. And you have given to the church a portion of whatever money you have earned outside of this service. No one has lived the principles of the gospel more faithfully."

The meeting was held on February 14th. Joseph Smith spoke to the assembled men, reminding them that it was time to perfect the organization of the church. Up to this time a group of three men had constituted the governing body: Joseph Smith as president, with two assistants or counselors. At this time these counselors were Sidney Rigdon and Frederick G. Williams. These three were called the First Presidency.

However, the new church was to have all the officers of the ancient church, and Twelve Apostles should now be appointed.

The elders listened quietly, but in every heart was the question, "Will I be one of them?" It would be a great honor to be named one of this select group, which would stand next to the First Presidency in the church hierarchy.

Brigham, of course, had no such question in his mind. Joseph Smith had told him that he would be named. He sat beside his friend Heber, and if there was a silent prayer on Brigham's lips, it was that this beloved friend be also chosen to work beside him.

The first name called was that of Lyman E. Johnson. He rose and went forward.

The second name rang out in the room: "Brigham Young!"

And then Brigham's heart leaped as the third name was announced. "Heber C. Kimball!"

Though their names were called in that order, their position in the quorum was determined by age rather than by the order of their calling. And as the other nine men were named, Brigham saw that his place was third from the top. Thomas B. Marsh and David W. Patten preceded him. The first would be president of the Twelve; the second would serve in this position when Marsh died, or left it for any other reason.

But Brigham was content. After the men had received a blessing and had been told what their duties would be as missionaries, Brigham turned to Heber and shook his hand warmly.

"Well, Brother Heber, this is a great day!"

Almost immediately the two friends had to part. Heber was sent to England to "open up the work" there. Brigham's mission was to New York and the New England States.

But before Brigham left on this mission, another thrilling event took place. His first son was born.

As he stood beside the big bed, the baby in his arms and his wife smiling up at him, Brigham felt that his happiness was too great for words. He reached down and gently lifted the long braid of light brown hair that lay over Mary Ann's shoulder. Putting it aside on the pillow, he laid the baby in the crook of his mother's arm, then kissed them both.

"Our son!" he murmured. "Born in the faith. He shall be called Joseph!"

Mary Ann smiled quietly. She had expected this, but she would have liked to call the boy Brigham. There were so many little Josephs in Kirtland! But it must be whatever Brigham wished.

In the fall Brigham returned from his mission and threw

himself wholeheartedly into church work in Kirtland. The thing of paramount importance that winter was getting the temple finished. Brigham's skill as a carpenter and his deftness as a painter were put to good use and the whole interior of the edifice shone with Brigham's handiwork. By March of 1836 it was ready to be dedicated.

Brigham looked with amazement and a deep sense of pride at the throng that assembled for the sacred event. The church was growing! Israel was gathering! Who could have guessed that so much could be accomplished in six short years?

William W. Phelps, the church hymn maker, composed a special song for the occasion. Brigham's heart lifted with joy as his rich voice joined the others, singing triumphantly:

"We'll sing and we'll shout with the armies of heaven,
Hosanna! Hosanna! to God and the Lamb!
Let glory to them in the highest be given
Henceforth and forever, Amen and Amen!"

Kirtland was growing and prospering and Brigham prospered with it. He had built a good house for Mary Ann and he had fashioned the furniture for it. His garden was excelled by none. His cows and horses, pigs and chickens were sleek and clean and healthy. He had plenty not only for his family, but enough left over to contribute generously to the common storehouse.

But this well-being was not to continue for long. As the Saints acquired more and more property, as they preached their religion more and more strenuously, the same antagonisms began to arise that had plagued their fellows in Missouri—and were still plaguing them.

As the old Missouri settlers had done, the people of Ohio began to view with alarm the growing numbers of Mormons. They knew that the Saints revered Joseph Smith and would do anything for him. They began to grow afraid of this man's power. What couldn't he do, with thousands at his beck and call?

Then, as more Saints poured in from the East and the North, as their city grew and their farms prospered, the grumbling changed to threats. These people would have to get out of Ohio.

And now there began to be trouble within the church. At first it wasn't too serious: bickering over minor authority, argument over the interpretation of the gospel, disagreement as to the meaning of certain revelations and commands.

Then something happened to intensify these little irritations. The financial panic of 1837 caused the church-sponsored Kirtland Safety Society to go bankrupt—as it had caused most of the nation's banks to do. But some church members, losing money, laid the blame entirely on Joseph Smith. It didn't mean anything that Gentile banks had gone under in the panic. That was to be expected. But that the Saints should lose money—that must be due to Joseph's carelessness, or worse.

Consequently, from within and without the church, faultfinding, dissatisfaction and threats mounted rapidly into a dangerous cloud that menaced the peace and happiness of the Saints at Kirtland.

And because Brigham believed that Joseph was a true prophet and should be obeyed unquestioningly, he was never silent or diffident about defending the leader. Naturally plain spoken, Brigham became curt and stern when irritated. And this bickering did irritate him.

At one meeting when some of the church members were grumbling because they were beginning to think Joseph had too much authority, Brigham stood up and shouted, "Joseph is a prophet and I know it. You may rail and slander him as much as you please, but all you will do is destroy your own authority, sink yourselves to hell!"

"You're as bad as he is!" someone yelled. "We'll get rid of you, too!"

The Ohioans, too, began to worry about Brigham. "He'd fight to the last ditch for that Joe Smith!" they said. "If we want to get rid of the Mormons, we'll have to grab a handful of the top men. If we get rid of those at the top, the rest will skedaddle back to their old homes."

Brigham considered his position and talked it over with Mary Ann.

"I've heard that they're trying to trump up some charge against me, in order to throw me into jail where I'll be helpless. And I don't intend to be thrown into one of their stinking jails—to bite my nails and wait for a trial that might never come. I can't be of any use to the Prophet if I'm locked away in a dirty little cell. But as long as I'm free, I can speak and act. Joseph and the church need as many loyal servants as they can find. So I'm going to get out before they can catch me."

"Where will you go, Brigham? And what about us?" She motioned toward the bedroom where the children were sleeping. There were five children now, for a pair of twins had been added to their family. Mary Ann had had her way in naming these babies, and the boy was Brigham, Jr.; his twin sister, Mary.

A look of tenderness came into Brigham's eyes. "You will go with me. To Missouri."

"But there is just as much trouble in Missouri—"

"Not where we are going. When the Prophet was out there this autumn he selected a new place—not in Clay or Jackson County. It's back farther from the river and hasn't been settled so thickly. He says it is the perfect place to build the new Jerusalem. A settlement is already begun near there—Far West—and Joseph has sent out word for those in the other communities to sell their property and gather to this new place."

Mary Ann sighed. "I wish the Prophet would be more careful. Perhaps he should have stayed in Missouri. There are such awful threats against him."

"He is going to return as soon as he can. So pack up what you'll need—the bare essentials. We'll leave tomorrow night."

Mary Ann said no more, but set about making ready for the long, wintry trip. And if she felt sadness at leaving her good house and fine garden, the furniture Brigham had fashioned so lovingly for her, and all the things they had acquired by thrift and hard labor, she gave no sign.

And the next night she was ready. Brigham brought a wagon to the back door of the cottage, and in the darkness they put into it the food and clothing they would need for the journey. The children were snuggled down warmly on straw in the wagon bed, with Mary Ann's carefully pieced quilts over them.

When everything was in place, he helped Mary Ann up onto the high seat. Then he quietly closed the cottage door and stepped up over the wheel to sit beside her.

It was snowing lightly as Brigham lifted the lines and clucked softly to the horses. As they moved out of the yard and into the road, Brigham put his arm about his wife.

"Don't look back, my dear," he said gently. "Our life lies ahead."

He bent to kiss her and found her cheek wet under his lips.

"You are not crying?" he asked tenderly.

Mary Ann brushed her hand across her face.

"No, I am not crying, Brigham. It's just the snow—"

The wagon moved slowly down the road through the thickening snow.

CHAPTER SIX

DRIVEN FROM MISSOURI

≫≫-≫≫-≫≫-≫≫-≫≫-≫≫-≫≫-≫≫-≫≫-≫≫

Brigham and his family had been gone only a few days when Joseph Smith also left Kirtland. Traveling faster than the apostle, he soon caught up with Brigham and they went on together toward Far West, the new settlement. It took them three months to make the long, tedious journey, so spring was breaking when they approached the Mormon community.

They found affairs in desperate shape.

Hundreds of families were homeless, living in the woods or in dugout holes along the riverbank, for the Missourians were determined that the Mormons would have to get out of the state altogether. They had continued to burn houses, steal cattle and destroy the crops of the harassed Saints.

Brigham looked at the misery and confusion and knew that something would have to be done to bring order out of the chaos. He set a good example himself by purchasing a small farm and setting immediately to work to fence and cultivate and plant it. He built a house and kept his family intact and well cared for.

Brigham held aloof from the Missouri troublemakers. He showed neither hostility nor friendliness, but went quietly and steadfastly about his own business. In this way he was able to learn much of what the Missouri groups were planning. The information he gathered was of great help to the Saints, and would have been more help still, if some of the hotheaded leaders among them had been willing to follow Brigham's example.

But since they didn't, the clashes continued and grew more bitter and deadly. The mobs, inflamed and frenzied past the point of thinking and acting as they normally would, began to beat and murder the Mormon settlers, while the Mormons, in self-defense, tried to organize their men to protect their communities. They appealed to the state authorities for assistance.

One autumn day a messenger came riding to Brigham's house.

"The militia is coming!" he shouted. "The state troops are on the way!"

Brigham looked at his friend Heber, who had just returned from his mission to England.

"Thank heaven!" he breathed. "They have come to aid the Saints." He rose, reaching for his hat. "Let's go into Far West and see what we can do to help."

The two friends hastened toward the town square. As they neared this place they could see that the excitement was all centered on the far side of the village. The roads were jammed with people. Mormons were hurrying along in groups, though the governor had warned them that they must not collect in crowds—"not even so many as five together!" From the opposite direction came swarms of "old settlers," crowding the heels of the horses of the mounted troops drawn up in military array across the stream that bounded the community.

"You're too late!" someone called to Brigham and Heber. "The leaders have gone out to parley with General Lucas."

"What's that?" Brigham asked. "Everything is to be settled peaceably?"

"Yes, thank heaven! General Lucas sent for the Prophet and Hyrum and Brother Sidney Rigdon and a few others. They'll be back soon. We'll be given back the arms that were confiscated by the soldiers. Everything is going to be all right!"

Brigham looked across the river to where the troops were. He could not see Joseph and the others, but something about the whole arrangement set his shrewd mind alert.

"Can you believe it's all right, Heber?" he asked. Then he added bluntly, "I can't. They have delivered the Prophet into the hands of our enemies. They won't let him come back."

Heber stared at him. "If he doesn't come back, you realize what that will mean?"

"It will mean that the Saints will have to get out of Missouri as fast as possible."

"And it means you will have to lead them out. You will be the virtual head of the church—"

As Brigham frowned, not comprehending, Heber went on, "With Joseph and Hyrum and Sidney in jail, the First Presidency will be powerless, and the Twelve will be at the head of the church. Marsh, who was president of the Twelve, has pulled up stakes and left, as you know. Captain Fearnought was killed on Crooked River. You are next in line, Brigham. You'll have to face it."

Heber was right. Joseph and his companions were taken away to jail; Governor Lilburn Boggs of Missouri advised the Mormons to get out of the state; and Brigham Young found himself in charge of some twelve thousand homeless, desperate and destitute people.

"The first thing to do," Brigham said grimly, "is to organize. Those who have food and conveyances will have to share with those who have not."

He called the elders together and told them, "I want you all to make a sacred covenant that we will stand by each other to the utmost of our ability in removing from this state. And that we will never desert the poor and worthy until they shall be out of the reach of their enemies!"

The men raised their right hands and promised.

"And now," Brigham went on, "sell your property if you can; or trade it for horses, oxen, wagons. Make ready to move."

"Where shall we go?"

"Illinois and Iowa have offered us shelter. The Prophet has told me he thought we should go to Illinois."

While they were talking, a messenger came posthaste. "They're after you, Brother Brigham! They want to put you in jail, too! They're taking all the leading men they can find. Oh, don't let them take you!"

"I won't let them get me," Brigham promised. "I've never thought a man could do much good when he was in chains."

Brigham kissed his wife good-by. "I'll go up to Illinois, find a place for us to gather. But I'll be back to lead you to that place!"

Brigham hurried northward to a small trading post called Commerce, on the banks of the Mississippi River, where the state of Illinois had offered to sell the Mormons some land. Across the river in Iowa, more land was available.

Some of the Missouri Saints were already making their way to this haven.

"Buy up land on both sides of the river," Joseph Smith had advised. "We want to make it impossible for anyone who doesn't like us to build right across from us." Brigham arrived at the new settlement, saw that the people were safe, and demanded, "Give me wagons, teams and provisions. I'll go back and help others to come to this place."

Without resting, he set out immediately on the backward trail. As he neared Far West he met wagons loaded with Saints, who were fleeing from their homes. Governor Lilburn Boggs of Missouri had issued what the Saints knew as the "exterminating order." This was his final word on the troubles there: The Mormons would have to leave the state

or be exterminated, unless they would renounce their religion.

When Brigham heard the governor's order he felt as the
other Saints did. It was an impossible demand. Not one of
them would renounce his religion. So they were leaving their
homes and crops and were trying to reach Illinois. But they
were improperly prepared for the journey. Escaping in haste
and fear, they had not had time to lay in provisions for the
trip. Brigham found the women and children crying and
hungry; the men harassed, but determined. He gave some
assistance to each group; advised them what road to take,
where to camp, what to do when Illinois was reached. And
then he hurried on.

And suddenly he saw on the road his own team and wagon.
Mary Ann was sitting on the high seat, holding a baby in
her arms. A neighbor was driving. Between them sat little
Brigham. When Mary Ann saw her husband, her face lighted
with joy. The children let out whoops of delight.

"Pa! Pa!" Now that he was here there would be nothing
to worry about. Brigham leaped from his wagon and went
to his family. His brow was creased with anxiety.

"What are you doing here?" he asked worriedly. "I told
you I would come back and get you."

"I know. But we could not wait. We had to get out—
everyone had to leave immediately."

Brigham's eyes went to little Mary, who lay pale and
limp against her mother's breast.

"What's the matter with Mary?" He bent over the child.

"The road is so bad! The wagon almost tipped over back
there a way. She was thrown out of my arms and the wheels
passed over her."

Brigham took the little girl from her mother's arms. He
brushed the hair back from the white face. There was sooth-
ing in his touch, and the child opened her eyes and smiled
at her father.

"You drive my wagon," he said to the neighbor. "I'll drive this one. I'll go back a piece with you and get you onto a good road."

Still holding Mary, he climbed up beside Mary Ann and took the lines. The children in the wagon stood up and crowded forward. They put their arms about their father, took hold of his shirt, tried, somehow, to touch him, to hold him.

"I could have driven the wagon, Pa!" Joseph said stoutly, "Only the road was so bad that Ma was afraid—"

Brigham smiled at his eldest son. Not yet four, yet eager to do a man's job.

"Well, Joseph, you can spell me off, maybe, in a little while!"

He lifted the lines, slapped them against the horses' backs and the wagon rolled forward. Under his careful hands, the animals found the best way between rocks and ruts and the wagon stopped its perilous pitching.

Toward evening they came to a small village, and Brigham went from house to house seeking shelter for his desperately weary wife and children, and for the women and children in the wagons that had fallen in behind him until he was leading a small caravan. Some of these had broken down beside the road; others had been uncertain which way to go; still others, farther back, hearing that Brigham had come, whipped up their teams to catch up with the apostle. And now they waited for him to find lodging for them all.

But there was no lodging. No one would take them in. Desperate, Brigham looked around him and saw an old, empty, dilapidated shed in a field.

His eyes lighted and he said cheerfully, "We'll stop here tonight. The Lord has provided a shelter."

"It's not much better than the open field!" one of the men grumbled.

Brigham's eyes grew frosty. "The Lord has provided a shelter. Now it is up to us to do our part. Let's get to work!"

He rolled up his sleeves and began. While the women tended the children and cooked supper over a campfire, the men obtained whitewash. They swept and scrubbed the barn, tore up the filthy floorboards and turned them over. They nailed the roof boards in place. And they whitewashed the building, inside and out.

Mary Ann, looking up from her cooking and seeing the energy with which Brigham was going about this task, and the miracle of a strong shelter he was bringing forth before her eyes, thought of the hymn the Saints had been singing: "The Spirit of God like a fire is burning!"

No one could accomplish such wonders without that burning spirit.

By dark, the shed was snug and clean. The women accepted the shelter gratefully. They prepared the tired children for bed. Then they sat around on the rough floor and sang:

> "Redeemer of Israel, our only delight,
>   On whom for a blessing we call;
>   Our shadow by day and our pillar by night,
>   Our King, our Deliverer, our All!"

They remained here two days, resting, washing clothes, baking bread. Then Brigham advised them to move on.

"We'll maintain this place as a way station," he said. "It will encourage the Saints to know that there is a place for them to rest and recuperate."

When he came to tell his family good-by, they clung to him as if they would never let him go. Brigham's eyes were tender, but his voice was cheerful.

"Why, Joseph! You're most a man, now. You take care of your mother and the girls." The little fellow's shoulders straightened. Brigham looked deep into Mary Ann's eyes. "I wish I could go on with you, but there are so many that need help. With the Prophet in prison, I must do everything I can—God will watch over you and protect you. And I will come just as soon as I can."

Mary Ann smiled quietly. "We must all do our part. Do not be anxious for us, Brigham. We're in the Lord's hands."

Brigham watched the wagons wind away northward, and then, setting his jaw grimly, he drove on to Far West.

In December of '39 Joseph and his companions escaped from the jail at Liberty, Missouri, and made their way to Illinois. There they found the Saints hard at work, building homes, caring for the sick and destitute—of which there were many—and already shaping up a settlement. And they were looking to Brigham for advice and encouragement. Without ostentation, he had assumed the role of leader in the absence of the Prophet.

One April day Joseph, Brigham and Joseph's brother Hyrum stood on a high bluff overlooking the Mississippi River. The late afternoon sun threw a golden patch across the water and laid a faint halo on the lowlands beyond.

"It's a beautiful place!" Joseph exclaimed with enthusiasm. "The most beautiful my eyes have beheld for a long time."

Brigham nodded, but his eyes were clouded. "The lowlands stink of the ague!"

"We'll drain them, then. We'll build a city that will be the largest and most beautiful in Illinois," Joseph answered. "Nauvoo—that means The Beautiful—it shall be called. Look!"

He unrolled before them a paper on which he had sketched the city of his dreams. There it lay, caught protectively in the deep bend of the river—a city of wide, tree-shaded streets, square blocks laid out to lie due north and south and east and west.

"Here, on this height where we now stand, we'll build our temple!" Joseph said. "Gleaming white, it will be seen for miles around!"

Brigham thought of the Kirtland temple which they had built with such labor and pain. It had been finished and dedicated late in March of 1836, only a year and a half before they had had to abandon it and go to Missouri. And here they were, driven from Missouri, too, and planning a new city and a new temple.

But no doubt shadowed Brigham's eyes as he looked at his beloved leader. "If you say it is to be so, Brother Joseph, so it will be. But we must roll up our sleeves and go to work—those swamps will have to be drained!"

CHAPTER SEVEN

SUCCESS IN ENGLAND

>>>->>>->>>->>>->>>->>>->>>->>>->>>->>>

Brigham Young's estimation of the unhealthy effects of the low swamplands was unhappily proved correct. Before autumn, half of Nauvoo was down with malaria, or chills and fever, as the people called the disease. Joseph Smith took the ailing people into his home and his yard until the place looked like a hospital. He and his wife cared for them night and day. Finally, Joseph, too, became ill.

In his small cabin across the river in the settlement called Montrose, Brigham and his whole family were desperately sick. Not one of them was able to go to the well for a pail of water.

Joseph arose from his own bed and came across the river to Brigham's house. He stood in the doorway, tall and handsome in spite of his pallor. He quietly surveyed the room filled with sick people.

"Arise, Brother Brigham, and come with me," he said.

Brigham shivered. Then he put his feet to the floor, stood up on trembling legs and followed Joseph. They went from cabin to cabin doing what they could to relieve and cheer the sufferers.

Earlier in the summer, Joseph had started some of the apostles on their missions. Those who had already been to England, Heber among them, had reported that that country was particularly ready to listen to the teachings of the Mormons. Now Joseph decided to send several of the Twelve to England. Some of these were already in New York waiting for the others to arrive. They did not wish to leave until Brigham, president of the group, could go with them.

In September, though he was still very ill, Brigham decided that he must be up and about the work to which he had been called. He could not keep his brethern waiting any longer.

Mary Ann, who was sick with the fever and had a newborn baby, looked at her feeble children around her. Then she turned to study the gaunt face of her husband.

"How can you go now, Brigham? You are still shaking with the ague. You have no clothes—"

"I'll wear what I have," Brigham answered stoutly.

"But the nights are cold, even though the sun is hot. You haven't even a hat."

"Well," Brigham said smiling wanly, "I never had much of a hat when I was younger. What do I need with one now? I used to make my own straw hats for summer, and in the winter my sisters would make what we called a Jo Johnson cap. I got along all right."

Mary Ann's eyes brightened. "There's an old pair of pantaloons—too far gone for much use. I thought of making Joseph some trousers from them, but there may not be enough material for that. I can make you a cap of sorts." She looked at their oldest son, just able to stagger about the room, he was so weak. "Can you find them for me, Joseph?"

Joseph found the old pantaloons, and then, sitting up in bed beside her tiny baby, Mary Ann cut and sewed a cap for her husband. When he put it on, the children giggled in spite of their misery.

"You look funny, Pa!"

Brigham stooped and kissed his wife. "I never had a handsomer cap!" he asserted. "Now, if only I had an overcoat—"

"There's nothing we can spare but the quilt from the trundle bed."

"Well, then, the quilt it must be!"

Brigham, in his homemade cap, with the small patchwork quilt about his shoulders, was ready to go to England. He had no money, no extra clothing. But he was confident that everything would be taken care of in due time. He kissed his ailing family good-by.

But when he got to the doorway he found he was too weak to make his way to the ferry a few rods distant. A neighbor hurried up to him and helped him down to the waiting boat.

As Brigham settled himself in the skiff to be rowed across the river to Nauvoo, the neighboor sighed and shook his head. "If we all had your grit and faith, Brother Brigham, nothing could stop this church!"

On the other side, Israel Barlow took Brigham up behind him on his horse and carried him to the house of Heber Kimball. The effort to get this far had taken every ounce of strength the sick man had.

Heber looked at his friend. "You can't make it, Brigham!"

"I don't know that word can't! I can do anything the Lord wants me to do."

But it was four days before Heber would start out with his ailing friend.

At last Brigham would wait no longer. A neighbor boy had been obtained to drive them in his father's wagon for the first day's journey. Then the boy would return, and other friends would carry the apostles on their next day's stretch. The wagon bed had been covered thickly with straw and old quilts placed there for Brigham to lie upon. When he was helped into the wagon he sank down with a sigh. Heber climbed in beside him.

At Heber's doorway a number of the Saints had gathered to wish the missionaries farewell. Many of these were so sick they could scarcely stand. As the wagon went along the wide street of Nauvoo, others appeared in their doorways, waving and shouting, "Hosanna! Good luck! God be with you, Brethren!"

"We ought to answer all those good wishes," Heber observed wistfully.

Brigham propped himself up on his elbow and waved his homemade cap feebly. Then he summoned all his strength and shouted in a voice so weak it could scarcely be heard above the rumbling of the wagon, "Hurrah! Hurrah for Israel!"

By slow stages they made their way across Illinois, Ohio, New York, stopping with Mormon families whenever possible, preaching as they went. It seemed miraculous to them that their needs were always met—somehow, money was handed to them, clothes were provided, food was set before them as they traveled, penniless, across the country. And as they went, Brigham's strength gradually returned.

It was a bitter winter night at the close of January when four ragged, gaunt apostles knocked on the door of 58 Mott Street in New York City. Parley Pratt, a fellow apostle, opened the door. He shouted in delight.

"Brother Brigham! You have come! God be praised!"

Brigham and Heber, John Taylor and George A. Smith crowded into the small room. Mrs. Pratt bustled about preparing food.

"I've been expecting you for weeks, now!" Parley said.

Brigham chuckled. "It's only taken us four and a half months to get here from Nauvoo. And we started out only two—and arrive four! That's not bad. Heber and I picked up Brother John and Brother George along the way."

"Well, now you're here, we can make plans for sailing at once."

Brigham smiled wryly. "Do I understand that you have passage money for us all, Brother Parley?"

Parley gasped. "How could I have?" he asked.

"Well, we haven't a penny. We'll have to tarry here in

New York until we earn enough to pay our passage across the ocean. How much will it cost?"

"I've found out all that," Parley said eagerly. "We can travel steerage for eighteen dollars each, if we furnish our own bedding and provisions. Of course, we'll have to pay the cook something for preparing our victuals. But I think we can make it on twenty dollars each."

"What about ships?"

"I have a list here. Let's see, how much time will you need, Brother Brigham?"

"Perhaps a month—"

"Well, the *Patrick Henry* will sail on March 9th. Do you think—"

"We'll set that as our goal. If you have a goal, you can at least try to make it," Brigham said decisively. "We'll have the sisters get to work and make us each a straw mattress and pillow. And we'll go out in the city and find jobs—any kind of jobs—to provide the necessary cash. If we can sail sooner than March 9th, we will. But we'll put that date as the very limit."

On the morning of March 9th a curious caravan made its way to the New York docks. There were six poorly dressed men, each carrying on his back a rolled up bed ticking stuffed with straw. In their arms were various bundles and parcels. Crowding along with the six were other men and some women and children. All of them carried bundles, too. Parley's wife clung to him, weeping. She wanted very much to go to England with her husband.

At the dock a small boat was waiting to carry the missionaries to the ship, which lay farther out. The six apostles shook hands with their friends, stepped into the skiff and deposited their mattresses and bundles about them. The boatmen shoved off.

On the shore the little band of watchers waved their handkerchiefs and began to sing the "missionary song."

"The gallant ship is under weigh
    To bear us off to sea;
And yonder floats the streamer gay
    That says she waits for me."

"I go, it is my Master's call,
    He's made my duty plain;
No danger can the heart appall
    When Jesus stoops to reign.
And now the vessel's side we've made,
    The sails their bosoms swell,
Thy beauties in the distance fade—
    My native land, farewell!"

The missionaries stood up in the boat and joined in the song, singing more enthusiastically than the watchers on the shore.

The missionaries were crowded in the steerage. Their eighteen-dollar passage money allowed only three berths for the six men—the four from Nauvoo and Parley and Orson Pratt. Into their crowded quarters they settled down for the month-long journey across the Atlantic. It didn't matter greatly to Brigham that they were so cramped. He was sea-sick nearly all the time.

When the brethren left the ship at Liverpool, Brigham bought a ticket to Preston, the church headquarters in England. This done, he found he had "six bits" left. He took off his homemade cap, looked at it, then handed it to a beggar. Then he went into a store and bought himself a hat.

The British mission had been headed by Wilford Woodruff, who was deeply engrossed in writing a history of the church. Now Brigham, as president of the twelve Apostles, took charge. With his characteristic energy he put new life into the mission and new ambition into the converts.

He sent out word, "We will hold a general conference at Preston on the 15th and 16th!"

"But you've just arrived!" someone argued. "Hadn't you better look around first?"

"We'll have been here ten days by then. I want to meet the people, find out what they want and need."

"But how are we to get to Preston, if we have no money for railroad fare?"

"Walk! Many times I have walked hundreds of miles, in snow and freezing weather and with blood in my shoes, because the urge to preach the gospel was so strong in me. In this pleasant weather, anyone who can't walk to conference can stay away!"

The conference hall was packed. When Brigham rose to speak and looked out over the crowded room, he felt elated that so many had heard his call and had answered. But he felt sad, too. Most of these people were desperately poor. Brigham had nothing but sympathy and respect for honest poverty. But the church needed money. They should turn their attention to getting a few wealthier converts.

Brigham seemed inspired that day, as he talked to the Saints in the little hall at Preston. He told them about Joseph, the Prophet; about Nauvoo, the Beautiful; about America, the land of promise.

"There are thousands of acres there, as flat as a cultivated park, just waiting for the plow and the seed! We want the Saints to come to Zion and partake of the bounty and the joy there."

The listeners looked at each other. It sounded like Paradise.

"But how can we go? We have no money."

"If you want to go, a way will be opened. How did I and these brethren get here? When we left Nauvoo we had no money—less than ten dollars among us, and only the clothes on our backs. But here we are. If you do your part, the Lord will do His. I've had that proved to me again and again. Now, what else do you Saints desire?"

"A newspaper! We should have a newspaper to keep us in touch with each other, and to let us know what the authorities wish."

"You shall have a newspaper. Brother Parley, here, has already been thinking along those lines. He wants to be editor, and I so appoint him. He has chosen the name for this newspaper—The Millennial *Star*. He will start work on it at once."

"How can I publish a paper right now?" Parley whispered. "It may take a year to get enough subscribers to pay the cost—"

"You start it at once. I'll see that the bill is paid," Brigham answered confidently.

"We need copies of the Book of Mormon," Brother Wilford said. "I've inquired about shipping some from Nauvoo, but the duty is so high we can't afford it."

"Print them here, then, and sell them to the Saints. They won't cost the church anything that way."

"We need hymnbooks. The old hymns do not express what we feel."

"Print hymnbooks, then."

The English converts looked at this man. Nothing stood in his way. If there was something to be done for the church, he said "do it!" and that was the end of the discussion. The thing was done. They felt new hope.

"Go to John Benbow," one of the Saints said to Brigham. "He is a very wealthy farmer and is interested in Mormonism. He will help you get these projects started, I'm sure."

Brigham extended his hand. "Thank you, Brother. I knew a way would be opened to us."

He was right. He visited John Benbow and his wife Jane. He didn't ask for money, but he explained what was needed here in the British mission, and he didn't neglect to mention how scarce money was. He came away with a thousand dollars.

Brigham talked to other well-to-do Englishmen. More money flowed in.

"I love the poor Saints," he told Heber. "I understand them, having always been poor myself. But we need some with money; and we need craftsmen of all kinds if we are to build up Zion. There is no need to labor only among the poor."

Heber agreed wholeheartedly.

"And perhaps we can figure a way to help the poorer Saints get to Nauvoo," Brigham went on thoughtfully. "You know my belief has always been that we should help each other as much as possible. It works well; it got all the destitute Saints out of Missouri—and harmed no one. I believe that if a man uses his substance to help his brother, his substance is amplified and not diminished."

Heber looked at his friend. "How would you manage something like that here?"

"I see a clear way," Brigham said without hesitation. "Those with money would lend it to the church and the church would lend it to those who needed help in emigrating. When they got settled, they'd pay it back and it would be lent to some one else."

Heber nodded thoughtfully. "It sounds good."

"We'd have to set up an office, of course. We'd have to talk to ship owners, get them to give us the best possible rates. This is going to be a big business, Heber, emigrating Saints and shipping goods to Zion. We should be able to handle it."

Two months after his arrival in England, Brigham sent the first company of British emigrants to Nauvoo. There were only forty in that first group.

"But they are the pledge of more to come. Thousands shall

pour into Zion from the British Isles!" Brigham said enthusiastically.

As he went about preaching, Brigham kept to his economical ways. There were many beggars in the streets of every town.

"I've seen more beggars since I've been in England than I saw in all my life before I came here," one of the missionaries told Brigham.

Brigham always carried a few copper pennies in his pocket to hand to these beggars as he passed.

One day as he was going through a market, his eyes were caught by the stacks of fresh fruits and vegetables. Brigham stopped to look and to smell, his mouth watering. It had been a long time since he had tasted fresh fruit. He moved on, but paused again before a stall stacked with bunches of purple grapes.

Almost involuntarily, his hand went into his pocket and brought out a copper penny. He gave it to the stall-keeper for a bunch of the grapes. Breaking them off one by one, he ate them slowly, savoring the fresh, tangy sweetness of the fruit.

He had just crushed the last grape on his tongue, when a beggar woman came by, her clawlike hand extended, her voice whining.

Again Brigham's hand went into his pocket, but it was empty. He had spent his last penny for the grapes.

"That won't ever happen again," he told Heber that night. "I was ashamed that I had yielded to temptation and spent money on something that was not necessary."

Brigham remained in England a little more than a year. When he was ready to return to America, he summed up what he and his companions had done in that short time.

"We've printed five thousand copies of the Book of Mormon and sold enough of these to pay back the money Brother John Benbow and other Saints let us have. We have printed three thousand hymnbooks and sixty thousand religious tracts and pamphlets. Each month we have published two thousand copies of the Millennial *Star*. We've paid for board and lodgings and have obtained a house for Brother Willard Richards, who will tarry here. We have given Brother Parley enough money to bring his wife over to stay with him. We have given six hundred dollars toward helping the poor Saints emigrate to Zion and we have seen a thousand souls leave Liverpool for Nauvoo.

"We're leaving two thousand dollars worth of books in the office here, a well-established newspaper, many flourishing branches, all perfectly organized. We have baptized eight thousand people.

"Now we return to our families, but we leave you in good hands. Be strong in the faith; be diligent in good works; and gather to Zion as speedily as possible!"

CHAPTER EIGHT

THE MANTLE OF JOSEPH

⇒⋙-⋙-⋙-⋙-⋙-⋙-⋙-⋙-⋙-⋙

When Brigham Young returned to Nauvoo from England in July of 1841, he found his family destitute and suffering. They had moved across the river to Nauvoo and were living in an unfinished cabin in a low, swampy part of the settlement. They were hungry and ragged.

If Brigham felt angry at this, he gave no sign. He set to work at once to better the situation. He fenced his property, finished the cabin and plowed his land. When he first tried to plow he found the ground so wet that the oxen mired in it and could not do the work. So Brigham set about draining the land to make it fit for cultivation. He wanted to build a substantial brick house for his family and intended to do so, but before he had started on it, Joseph Smith came to the cabin.

"Brother Brigham," Joseph said, "I am well pleased with your labors in England. It is no longer required of you to leave your family as in times past. Take special care of your family from this time on."

Brigham smiled gratefully. Then he shook his head rather ruefully. "There are so many tasks to be done for the church. I'll help with those, too. I can build my house if I have just a little time now and then."

So he continued to attend to the many duties that rested on him as president of the Quorum of Twelve Apostles. This group, second only to the First Presidency, had charge of all missionary work and of caring for the emigrants that poured in from the various branches. They also were overseeing the vast building program that was turning Nauvoo into the largest and finest city in Illinois. By no means the least of Brigham's duties was taking charge of the building of the new temple. But his tremendous energy, his habits of orderliness, his avoidance of wasted time and effort all combined to help him accomplish far more than the average man could do.

During the next three years he became one of the best-known figures in the area—the person to whom any member of the church could go for assistance and advice and not be turned away. He made many short trips into the surrounding branches of the church. And always he urged the people to support Joseph Smith, not only by faith and prayer but by tangible ways as well.

"If you have any surplus food or stock, send them in to the Prophet Joseph. We must release him from all worry about the necessities of life, so he can be free to do the Lord's work!" He asked nothing for himself or his family, and he received nothing for his church work.

He found homes for the hundreds of emigrants that poured into the new Zion. He attended all the council meetings, giving excellent and practical advice. Among other things he told the men of the church, "Do not leave your families to go on missions unless you have a good roof over their heads and a year's store of provisions on hand."

When someone muttered at this, Brigham turned to him. "Do not say 'Brother Brigham left his family sick and without food.' Brother Brigham had a special call. He obeyed it. He did his part and the Lord did His. But the Lord isn't calling on you to do the same thing. And we have our hands full enough. Take care of your own families before you leave them."

Nauvoo grew and prospered. There were ten thousand

people in the city itself, thousands more scattered in the outlying area. It was a city such as Joseph had planned, with wide, straight, tree-bordered streets, substantial houses surrounded by gardens, neat stores and schools. And on the hill above the town the temple was rising, a gleaming white building standing out against the blue sky.

But in spite of all the busyness and prosperity, Nauvoo was not peaceful. Again the neighbors of the Mormons were growing restless. Joseph Smith, they said, had too much power for any church leader. Nauvoo had been granted a charter by the state of Illinois. This charter gave the community many special privileges that the neighboring settlements did not enjoy. And, while every little town had its own troop of soldiers for protection against the Indians and other dangers of the frontier, the Nauvoo Legion was by far the best equipped and the best drilled little army in the entire state. The Mormons, their neighbors said, were becoming altogether too strong economically and politically.

"That army of theirs could easily defeat all the other troops in Illinois!" they grumbled. "They could easily make their leader, that Joseph Smith, a ruler with more power than our governor—or even the President of the United States!"

"They'll do it, too!" others agreed angrily. "Why, they'd follow their Prophet even against their country! They can't be loyal Americans! Look at their army! What are they drilling for? They're planning something, you can lay to that!"

"We never should have let them come into the state! Softhearted we were, thinking they were persecuted in Missouri!"

"Softheaded, rather—letting them get a foothold here! Then they go out and drag in converts from all over the world. Set 'em all to work—build a big city—biggest city in Illinois. We're at their mercy, I tell you! We gave them that charter—Nauvoo is like a state, not a city. Has its own army, its own officers of the law, its own laws and its own religion. All those Mormons vote the way Joe Smith tells 'em to. Last election they ran the whole show—put in the men they wanted. Next time they'll put Joe Smith in as governor—"

"Or president! Or king! We've got to stop 'em!"

And there was another thing that was causing gossip. During this period, Joseph Smith had told the leaders of the church that he had had a revelation in which he had been commanded to restore the ancient marriage system. Like Abraham and Solomon, the elders were to have more than one wife. This principle was not announced publicly at this time, but as the leaders accepted it and put it into practice, rumors began to float about. And like most rumors, the stories were greatly distorted. However, the gossip gave the enemies of the Saints a powerful, emotional weapon against the church.

In June of 1842 Brigham married Lucy Ann Decker as his first plural wife. As time passed, he married others, as did his friend Heber Kimball and other church leaders. And, though the facts were not generally known, many outside of the church listened to the whispering campaign that soon started.

And then in 1844, not approving of the policies of any of the candidates for president of the country, the Mormons decided to have their own leader Joseph Smith run for that office. Some three hundred Saints volunteered to go about the country campaigning for their candidate. The supervision of this work was given to Brigham Young. He went to New England to campaign actively, while directing the work of the others.

One July evening Brigham was in Petersboro, Vermont, with Orson Pratt. They went to the home of one of the Saints there, a Brother Bement.

"President Young!" Bement said when he saw his visitors.

He gave Brigham the title accorded him as president of the Twelve Apostles. "What are you doing here? I thought you would be on your way to Nauvoo. Haven't you heard?"

A sense of disaster filled Brigham. "Heard what?"

"Come in! Come in! I'll let you read for yourself this letter from Brother Joseph Powers."

Brigham and Orson stepped inside. With trembling hands their host unfolded a letter and handed it to Brigham. The apostle read it slowly, scarcely able to grasp its contents.

The letter told how Joseph Smith and his brother Hyrum had been assassinated by a mob. The two church leaders had gone to Carthage, the county seat, to answer charges of treason which had been made against them. The brothers, with two of the apostles, had been thrown into jail, and a mob had formed while they were there. They had broken into the jail and shot and killed the two Mormon leaders.

As Brigham read, anger tightened his throat. Tears filled his eyes. He had loved Joseph Smith with an intense devotion and reverence. He could scarcely believe that anyone would dare to kill so holy a man. Mobs! Mobs! They had robbed the world of its choicest spirit!

Then a startling thought pierced his sadness. What of the church? Had Joseph taken the keys of the kingdom with him? Would it be possible to go on? Would there be more revelations of God's will? Brigham's thoughts darted this way and that, seeking the answer to these questions.

Suddenly he struck his knee with his clenched fist. "No!" he almost shouted. The others looked at him questioningly.

"We hold the keys to the kingdom," Brigham went on positively. "When Joseph ordained the Twelve he conferred upon us all the authority, all the powers, he possessed. The church can go on!"

Then, realizing the loss his beloved church had suffered, he bent his head and wept.

Brigham knew that the people in Nauvoo were now with-

out a real leader. He had seen them leaderless before, and
he knew what confusion and trouble arose when this happened. Since Hyrum had been closest to Joseph, it was
generally thought that he was to follow his brother as head
of the church. But Hyrum was dead. Who was left?

Sidney Rigdon would probably consider himself the
leader. Rigdon had been one of the most powerful men in
the first days of the church. A former Baptist minister,
Rigdon had been converted to the Church of Jesus Christ
of Latter-day Saints when he was living at Kirtland. It had
been largely due to his influence that Joseph Smith had
chosen Kirtland when he left New York State.

But Sidney Rigdon was a dangerous man to head the
Saints in these troubled times. He was a powerful orator,
but he did not always use the best judgment in making his
speeches. It had been an adress of Rigdon's in Missouri that
had been the match to light the tinder of the mob's anger.
Brigham felt a sort of terror when he thought of the harm
this fanatical old man could do.

The welfare and happiness—the very lives—of more than
fifteen thousand people were at stake. A man was needed,
a man firm in the gospel and powerful in leadership. As
president of the Twelve, the responsibility devolved upon
him.

Brigham dashed the tears from his eyes and rose.

"We must get back to Nauvoo at once."

He sent word to the apostles who were traveling to return
at once to Nauvoo. Nothing must delay them. Some were
already there. Dr. Willard Richards and Elder John Taylor
had been with Joseph and Hyrum in the Carthage jail. John
Taylor had been injured during the shooting and Dr.
Richards had taken charge of affairs in the absence of any
higher authority.

With his companions Wilford Woodruff, Orson Pratt and
Orson Hyde, Brigham hastened back to Nauvoo. They

traveled day and night, changing from train to boat to steamer to stage—anything to cover the ground most rapidly. They arrived on the evening of August 6th and stared in sorrowful amazement at the bereft city. When they had left, only ten weeks before, it had been buzzing with activity and industry. Now it lay dark and still. The streets were empty, the windows shuttered, the farms untended.

Brigham and his companions hurried through the deserted streets to Brigham's house. They sent out for the rest of the Twelve to join them there.

It was a sober group that met that evening in the big front room of the sturdy brick house Brigham had found time to construct. As president of the quorum, Brigham began at once. Turning to those who had been in Nauvoo throughout the trouble, he asked, "What is the situation here, Brethren?"

Willard Richards answered. "Everything is quiet, so far. At first our enemies figured we would try to get revenge—maybe kill Governor Ford—for he was right here in Nauvoo and it could have been done. But I advised the people to be quiet and orderly, to make no hostile move. I knew if they raised a hand we would all be wiped out."

"That was right. You did well."

Dr. Richards went on, "Brother Sidney Rigdon has come in from Pittsburgh. He is going about claiming he is to be the head of the church. He has asked the people to name him guardian. I've had a difficult time keeping him from getting this before the church membership. I am glad you brethren are here, as Brother Sidney has called a general meeting for day after tomorrow."

"Well, don't let him—or anyone else—know that we have returned. We'll be at that meeting. We'll let him put his plan before the people. Then I will speak."

His companions nodded, agreeing. Brigham was president of their group. He had every right to take the lead in this matter. And his decisiveness, his energetic handling of the situation, would be their only hope of saving the church. Every one of them was afraid to let Sidney Rigdon be the head of the church.

Two days later Nauvoo was again awake—but quietly and solemnly. Thousands of men, women and children moved silently along the streets toward the open space in front of the half-finished temple, where the meeting was to be held. The wind was blowing up from the river. Prairie dust filled the air. But the Saints paid scant attention to this. There was more important business on hand.

In front of the temple was a raised platform, where the church authorities usually sat. Sidney Rigdon mounted it and looked out over the crowd below him. He seemed to be an old man, gaunt and trembling. He had been through all the trials and troubles of the church; had been in the Liberty jail with Joseph and Hyrum, and these things had made him old before his time. As he stood there, the wind blew his straggling gray hair and beard about his face. The people raised their eyes toward him and waited. There were some who felt that his cause was just. There were many who were remembering how he had disagreed with Joseph Smith and other church leaders, and how he had gone away, angrily, to Pittsburgh, leaving Nauvoo.

When Rigdon began to speak, the wind caught his words and beat them back into his face. His audience could not hear what he was saying. Observing this, he left the platform and went to the other side of the clearing. There he mounted a wagon bed. Now the wind was with him, carrying his voice over the crowd.

He had at one time been a fine orator, holding these same people spellbound with his eloquence. But that time was gone. He spoke in a rambling, uncertain manner. And as he talked on and on, the crowd grew restless.

After an hour and a half of this, he shouted, "I propose

to be a guardian to the people, and the people can suit themselves whether they accept me or not!"

The crowd stirred and muttered. They were restless and uncertain. Suddenly from behind them, above the murmuring came a clear, firm voice, "Attention, all!"

As one man they turned to face the regular platform. And there, his hand raised above them, in the attitude so often taken by their Prophet Joseph, stood Brigham Young.

This was the church as they knew it. To the amazed people it seemed as if their beloved Prophet stood there again before them.

"It is Joseph!" a woman's voice cried out. The cry was taken up by a thousand throats. "It is Joseph! The mantle of Joseph has fallen upon his shoulders!"

Brigham raised his hand in Joseph's familiar gesture for silence. The crowd, awed, became utterly still.

Miraculously, the wind had died down. Brigham's voice was carried on the clear, quiet air to every listening ear. He spoke simply, forcefully and eloquently. It seemed to the awe-struck crowd that this was Joseph's voice they were hearing again.

At last Brigham said quietly, "I don't care who leads the church, but one thing I must know is what God wants done. In the hands of the Twelve are the keys for learning God's will."

There was no need for fear or helplessness, he told the people.

"The Prophet Joseph has laid the foundation for a great work and we will build upon it. There is an almighty foundation laid, and we can build a kingdom such as never was in this world!"

As Brigham paused the people nodded, agreeing. They didn't want a guardian; they didn't want hesitancy and fear. They wanted to go on as they had been—a living, working part of a living church. They wanted to help build up Zion.

Suddenly Brigham's voice rang out, "I will tell you who your leaders or guardians will be—the Twelve, I at their head!"

A tremendous shout filled the air, "Hosanna! Hosanna! Amen and Amen!"

"Those who wish to sustain the Twelve as the directing body of the church, manifest it by raising their right hand."

A sea of hands surged whitely over the crowd.

"Opposed?"

Ten hands fluttered feebly.

Sidney Rigdon climbed down from the wagon bed and slowly stumbled away.

CHAPTER NINE

FAREWELL, NAUVOO, THE BEAUTIFUL!

≫≫-≫≫-≫≫-≫≫-≫≫-≫≫-≫≫-≫≫-≫≫-≫≫

Brigham Young took hold of the church affairs with a firm hand and a steady purpose. There was no faltering, no fumbling. He knew exactly what he had to do: Build up Zion; save the people from their enemies; preserve the power and authority that had been handed down from heaven.

Brigham had supreme faith in the divinity of the church. But his practical mind saw the present task as one of construction. He freely admitted that Joseph had had the vision, had seen the perfect design. Now hardheaded work was needed to carry out this plan.

Two days after the meeting in front of the temple, he called his fellow apostles to a parley. They came at once, eager to hear the purpose of this determined and resourceful leader.

Brigham stood at the head of the table, around which the Twelve were seated. He was now forty-three years old, a rather square-built man, five feet ten in height, with a sturdy frame. His light auburn hair was worn parted on the left side and long enough to fall well over his ears. His blue eyes had never lost their keen, penetrating look, but now they were older and wiser. They could be gentle or humorous or shrewd. And they could flash with anger. Many a stouthearted Saint had quailed before that look when Brigham had found him derelict in his duties.

81

With women he was courteous and gentle. "I love to see them happy," he often said. And the women among the Saints found it easy to go to Brother Brigham with their troubles and anxieties. He, they knew, would take time to help them, and that his advice was sound.

The children loved him. Whenever he walked the streets of Nauvoo, a crowd of youngsters followed, some holding his hands, others running beside him, looking up into his face. And he would smile and joke with them.

He let his gaze rest now on each of his companions in turn, as he thought surely the church Joseph had founded was safe in the hands of such loyal and stalwart men. Joseph Smith, Brigham knew, had been an idealist. He had trusted a number of men who had turned out to be traitors to him and to his church. But Brigham's companions in the quorum now were men who had been with the church through all its trials; who had served in every capacity they had been called upon to serve; who were loyal in thought and word and act, and who would remain loyal to their death.

"We have our work laid out for us," Brigham began. "It is simply to carry out the plans made by the Prophet Joseph. We must finish the temple; we must continue to send missionaries to all parts of the world; and we must move the Saints out of Illinois and into the Rocky Mountains. These are our main objectives."

His listeners agreed. One of them remarked, "There will be some grumbling, Brother Brigham. Some will say that if we are going to leave Nauvoo, why should we finish the temple, just to abandon it to our enemies."

"Joseph said the temple should be completed. He said we should not hold another conference until that job was done. And he said we should not go to the mountains until we had received our blessings in that holy edifice. I intend to finish the work the Prophet began."

"But the Gentiles—I doubt if they will let us carry on that work in peace."

Brigham's voice was hard. "We will build the temple in this place, even if we have to build as the Jews built, with a sword in one hand and a trowel in the other."

His companions nodded. "It shall be done, Brother Brigham."

"Now, as to our move to the West, we must prepare for it. We must work out every detail—have the move orderly and systematic, in order to eliminate as much suffering and hardship as possible."

"Have you decided where we are to go?"

"The Prophet decided that long ago. He said, 'To the Rocky Mountains,' and to the Rocky Mountains it shall be. We'll obtain maps and reports; we'll study the country. I understand that Captain John C. Frémont has gone out there exploring. We'll send a man to Washington to interview him."

Heber said, "You have plans for organizing—"

"Yes. I want the entire church organized at once into companies of one hundred, with a captain at the head. Each company is to bend every effort toward getting ready for the journey. We must send around to the different branches to get teams and wagons, and we must buy oxen, horses and provisions from the Gentiles. Here in Nauvoo we must plant every vacant foot of space to gardens or to grain. We must save as much of our produce as we can—live on short rations here to provide for the trip out. Every man, every foot of ground, must be utilized toward this and toward finishing the temple. They can work at either task, but all must work."

Before the council broke up that night, members had been appointed to oversee every phase of the two big projects. With the Twelve supervising the church work in Nauvoo, the missionary labors would be somewhat curtailed—but not abandoned. Wilford Woodruff was placed in charge of the British mission, John Taylor, Parley P. Pratt and Orson Hyde soon joining him there.

Brigham's energy and purpose seemed to be contagious. The people of Nauvoo set to work with a determination to fulfill all Brigham's demands. The little city in the bend of the Mississippi hummed day and night with the sound of ax and hammer, saw, plow, spinning wheel and churn. The gardens blossomed; the temple rose stone by stone.

The non-Mormons around Nauvoo watched these things with growing anxiety. They had been sure that as soon as Joseph Smith was out of the way, the Mormon church would fall to pieces. They had seen Sidney Rigdon go off to Pittsburgh with a handful of followers. They had watched one or two others rise up, claiming to be prophets, and leave Nauvoo with the few followers they could attract. Each time the neighbors of the Mormons had grinned and nodded. The Mormon church would soon be a thing of the past!

They had not counted on Brigham Young, however. His whole approach to the problem of church leadership was unexpected and frightening. He asked nothing for himself; he proposed nothing new. He simply went to work to carry out the plans made by Joseph Smith, and this assured him the loyalty and support of the vast majority of the church members.

"The Mormons aren't going to leave Illinois after all!" the watching neighbors said, shaking their heads. "Look at them—building that enormous temple. Would they do that if they were planning to leave?"

"You call that a temple? Looks to me more like a fortress. Those high stone walls—"

"Yea! And they're building a stone wall all around it, too. They're making ready to fight all of Illinois, you can lay to that!"

As winter came on and there were signs of ever-increasing

activity at Nauvoo, the people of Carthage and Quincy and Warsaw and other small towns near Nauvoo began to clamor in earnest for the removal of the Mormons. In January they persuaded the state legislature to cancel the city's charter. This left Nauvoo with no city government at all, since all officers were released with the revocation of the charter. It would have been a desperate situation for the fifteen thousand Mormons if the church authorities had not quietly assumed command and taken steps to preserve law and order.

The Mormons responded to their leaders and, on the whole, were especially careful to be law-abiding and orderly. But there was little they could do about the non-Mormons who seized upon the situation and came into the city to rob and plunder. And they had scant protection from law officers of other communities, who came with trumped-up charges against the Mormon leaders—with warrants for arrest and with demands for the surrender of the church authorities. Much of the time Brigham had to keep in hiding in order to avoid arrest on some spurious charge. But he still believed that he could do more good free than if he were in jail, and he did not intend to be arrested.

When the annoyance became too great, Brigham called Porter Rockwell, one of his loyal followers.

"Brother Porter," he said, "Can you suggest some way to handle these ruffians that come to make us trouble?"

"Leave it to me, Brother Brigham. I know how to scare those lily-livered scalawags out of town."

Porter called together the sons of some of the good church members. He talked to them a few minutes, then let them go.

The next fellow that appeared in Nauvoo with a warrant for the arrest of Brigham Young ran into something he hadn't bargained for. As he left the ferryboat, a young boy rose from beside the dock. Not looking at the stranger at all, the boy took from his pocket a sharp knife and a stick of wood. Whistling a merry tune, he walked along behind the stranger, whittling as he went. As if by magic, other boys came sauntering up. From yards, from side streets, from open doorways they came, whistling and whittling and saying nothing.

By the time the visitor reached the tavern he was practically surrounded by boys, all whistling and whittling merrily and disturbingly. He went into the tavern hoping the boys would go away. But when he came out there were even more of them. The man stared at them, but they paid no attention to him.

He started down the street and they swarmed along beside him, their knives glinting in the sun. Before he had gone far his nerve gave way. He turned and hurried back to the ferry. The last thing he saw as he was carried across the river was a group of giggling boys stuffing their knives into their pockets.

Brigham chuckled when he heard about his whistling brigade.

By May of 1845 the Nauvoo temple was ready for the capstone.

"Brother Brigham, maybe we should omit any ceremony. There are enemies in town with warrants for your arrest and that of the other apostles," Brigham was warned.

"We'll lay the capstone with suitable services," Brigham answered. "But we won't publish just when those ceremonies will take place."

On May 24th Brigham and his associates rose early. By six o'clock, while their enemies were still sleeping, the Mormons were at the temple. The capstone was laid. Brigham uttered a dedicatory prayer. As his voice rang out in the clear morning air the hundreds of Saints who had quietly gathered bowed their heads. And when Brigham finished, a great, triumphant shout arose, "Hosanna! Hosanna! Amen and amen and amen!" Joseph's temple would soon be built.

The sleeping deputies heard the shout and the singing that followed. They leaped from their beds, pulled on trousers and shirts and rushed to the temple. But Brigham and his associates were gone.

The Gentiles were more angry than ever. During that summer they began to burn the houses and crops of outlying Mormon families. In October they held an anti-Mormon meeting at Carthage, with nine Illinois counties represented. They presented a written ultimatum to Brigham. The Mormons must leave Illinois.

Brigham answered courteously but firmly. They were planning to go. They would leave in the spring. But they must have time to sell their property, harvest their crops and prepare adequately for the long journey to the mountains. It would not be an easy task to transport fifteen or twenty thousand people across the prairies and mountains. And they wanted time to give baptisms and perform the required rites in their new temple.

The anti-Mormon committee read Brigham's letter. "All right," they agreed, "you may wait till spring. And you may sell your property. But don't expect us to buy it."

Why should they buy it? they reasoned. When the Mormons were gone, they could walk in and take what they wanted.

Brigham Young called his entire family together—his wives and the children who were old enough to understand and help.

"I want you all to enter into this work with energy and confidence," he said cheerfully. "We must not only get ourselves ready for the trip west—wherever it is that we are going—but we must help others to get ready. And I will promise you this, I will do my best to keep you together and to see that you don't suffer unduly on the way. But you must do your part in preparing things for the journey. I won't have much time to help you there."

"Tell us what we should take, Brigham. We'll get it ready," Mary Ann said quietly.

"I am going to see that each family in Nauvoo and the near-by settlements has a list of necessities. I'll see that each of you has such a list, too. It will be based on families of five—and if you haven't five to care for of your own, two or three of you can team up and get the things together. I'll provide the wagons—the tools and implements and the seeds; you women will have to get the clothing, bedding, food, and so on. We'll want enough for a year, if possible—for five months at the very least."

Little Briggie looked up at his father. "Can I take my pet rabbit, Pa?"

"Yes, Brigham. Pet rabbits and doves and chickens can be taken along. And you can tell your friends that, too. We want you children to be happy on this journey—no mealy-mouths, no whimperers!"

Lucy spoke up, "My geraniums, Brigham. Would there be room for anything like that?"

"Perhaps not the geraniums," Brigham said gently. "But take slips of all the flowers that grow from slips—seeds of others. We'll want beauty. I'll make a list of the essentials and you can add whatever you can find room for."

"We'll do our best—"

Brigham's sunny smile lit up his face. "I know you will. But it isn't going to be easy. The Gentiles aren't going to sell us anything if they can help it. And what they sell they will charge heavily for. But use your good common sense, and do not let anything dismay you."

Brigham's wives, like the other women of the Mormon settlements, found that the leader had spoken truly. It was very difficult to purchase anything for the trip. And when it came to selling their property, they discovered that their neighbors were determined to get the best of every bargain. Sturdy red brick houses and gardens that had been the pride of Illinois had to be sold for almost nothing. A fine brick house with gardens and barns, worth at least eight thousand dollars, was traded for an old, worn-out team of oxen, a rickety wagon and a few chickens.

While the Saints worked feverishly to prepare for the journey, their neighbors continued to burn houses, barns and crops, to drive away cattle, to rob and plunder. Brigham appealed to the governor of the state and even to the President of the United States for protection. But nothing was done. Then he sent out word for all the outlying families to come in to Nauvoo. There, of course, they added to the burden already upon the Nauvoo Saints. But they accepted the burden. They saw Brigham, tireless as ever, going everywhere, advising, helping, and they felt inspired to do their own part cheerfully.

"If they will only give us till spring!" he said desperately. "If they will only keep their promise, I can move this entire people out of the state in order and safety."

Nauvoo became a hive of activity. Not only was the work on the temple progressing rapidly, but every house had been turned into a workshop of its own. Wagon beds were nailed together; wheels were fashioned; oxen yokes were shaped; nails and horseshoes were hammered out on ringing anvils. All day and all night, the sound of the hammer and the saw were heard. The midnight hours were lighted by the glowing forges.

The women were as busy as the men, spinning, weaving, cooking, quilting, making straw mattresses and pillows. And occasionally they took a hand at hammering or sawing.

By October the temple was finished enough so that the sacred rites could be held in that edifice. On the fifth of that month, five thousand Saints gathered to hold the first general conference in three years, as Joseph Smith had told them not to hold such a meeting until it could be held in the temple.

Before the religious services could be held or the sacred rites performed in the temple, Brigham offered a dedicatory prayer, presenting the temple, thus far completed, to the Lord as a monument of the Saints' liberality, fidelity and faith. He ended his prayer saying, "Lord, we dedicate this house and ourselves to thee."

That day and the following were spent in rejoicing that the Saints could now worship God within, rather than without, this sacred edifice which they were working so hard to build, even though they knew they must leave it as soon as it was finished.

This was the last conference, or general meeting, of the Saints in Nauvoo. By the time the temple was really completed and publicly dedicated on May 1, 1846, Brigham was camped at Garden Grove, one hundred and fifty miles from his beloved City of Joseph, with hundreds of his people already on the move to the West.

For as the temple neared completion the people of Illinois grew more and more insistent that the Saints leave the state. Brigham, playing for time, willingly showed how his people were making preparations to leave.

"I cannot move fifteen thousand souls out into unknown country without proper preparation," he argued earnestly. "But they will be ready by spring."

They were not to have till spring. In February, with the snow deep on the ground and the Mississippi River frozen over, the demands became so insistent they could not be ignored. The angry people came closer and closer to Nauvoo, their firebrands spreading terror and destruction.

At last, angered by the failure of the authorities to protect the Saints, Brigham cried, "We will go! We will go!"

He sent out the call, "To your tents, O Israel!" He was determined to keep his people aware of the religious significance of their move. He knew that only by that means could he weld them together into a unified and obedient mass. With thousands of people on the move, it would be difficult enough to maintain a high moral atmosphere and prevent bickering and thieving and taking advantage of others that would naturally sprout up among a vast, moving throng.

Early in February the first families set out across the Mississippi River. It was bitter cold that day, but a short warm spell had somewhat melted the ice on the river, so that the stream was filled with slush which in places was again freezing hard. Snow was falling, but the wagons moved out of Nauvoo, fought their way across the dangerous river on rafts and boats. The miserable people made camp in the snow on the Iowa side.

That first night, in the snow and the cold, nine babies were born. Their mothers lay in wagon beds, or on the ground, while the sleet pelted down on them. But the babies were lusty and all survived that terrible night.

On the morning of the 15th, Brigham himself made ready to leave Nauvoo, the City of Joseph, as he liked to call it. He brought the big wagon around to the front door of his home and helped the women and children settle themselves as comfortably as possible. His extra teams and cattle were driven behind the wagon by men who were glad to have a job with the leader, as they felt sure this would mean that they would not be the last into the new Zion. The river was now frozen over again, and Brigham had advised everyone who could to leave before another thaw.

As he drove away from the two-story brick home he had built with so much effort, he was joined by other families with their wagons and cattle. From his seat on his own wagon, Brigham looked along the road at the moving hundreds. The horses were tossing their heads, rattling bridle chains, neighing and whinnying. Oxen were lowing. Cows were mooing, chickens cackling, pigs squealing, dogs barking. And women and children were looking back and weeping.

Brigham stood up in his wagon and shouted in a voice that could be heard above all the racket, "Don't look back! Look Ahead! Zion is waiting beyond the mountains! Forward with stout hearts. The Camp of Israel is on the march!"

He flicked his horses with the whip and they stepped gingerly along. Brigham did not glance back at the City Beautiful with the temple shining white against the gray wintry sky.

CHAPTER TEN

"YOU SHALL HAVE YOUR MEN!"

Crossing the frozen Mississippi was an arduous task for the caravan of five hundred heavily loaded wagons. The oxen and horses slipped on the ice and fell to their knees. It was difficult to get them up onto their feet again, and each time an accident like that happened women screamed and children cried in fear. Snow and sleet and wind whipped into the desperate travelers.

On the farther bank of the river the confusion was still more appalling. Wagons had mired hub-deep in the prairie mud, soft under the snow. Children ran about crying with cold and hunger. Mothers were frantically trying to cook over sleet-quenched fires. Babies wailed; animals contributed their mournful cries of misery.

Brigham Young looked at the higgledy-piggledy camp and impatience surged through him. No effort had been made to establish order, to take care of sanitation problems, to provide even a minimum measure of comfort. It was just a huddled mass of miserable humanity, flung down in the snow beside the river, waiting for someone to tell them what to do.

"Drive on!" Brigham commanded his eldest son, now a sturdy twelve-year-old. "Drive on to Sugar Creek and make camp there. We can't stop in this mess."

Brigham himself climbed down from the wagon, mounted a horse and went through the disorganized camp.

"Pack up your things!" he commanded. "We are moving on to Sugar Creek to a clean camp."

Again and again he was out of the saddle, putting his shoulder to the wheel of a mired wagon, helping to load a heavy sack of provisions, carrying a crying child to its mother.

His energy put new life into the helpless camp. Men went to work with more courage and determination; women took new hope; children saw President Young and felt safer.

Four miles from the river the motley caravan came to the steep bluffs that separated the prairie from the stream. They were icy and dangerous, with mud under the thin frozen crust.

Porter Rockwell rode up to Brigham. "Some of the folks want to camp here," he said. "But there's a better place farther on, as I told you—Sugar Creek—if we can get the wagons up these bluffs."

"We can get them up!" Brigham answered. "Brother Porter, ride ahead, help those first wagons. Tell the drivers to double up and help each other. Tell my son Joseph to help his mother get settled—I'll be along later. But I'll stay here until the last wagon is up."

It was long past dark when Brigham finally came to that camp on Sugar Creek. He found his family already settled, a brisk fire going, fragrant meat stew bubbling in a kettle over the glowing coals. He smiled wryly. If only the other men had been foresighted enough to teach their families the rudiments of camp life before starting out on this hazardous journey!

He took a bowl of stew from Mary Ann's hands and sat down on an upended barrel. As he ate he looked about him.

"Where's your wash kettle?" he asked suddenly.

"In the wagon, Brigham. Why?"

"Get it out. Have the boys fill it up with water—clean

water. Get it boiling as soon as you can and make up a
kettleful of your herb tea!"

Mary Ann smiled understandingly. She spoke to her sons
and the boys, though they had been doing man's work all
day, set about the new task. Their mother hung the kettle
on a crane over the fire, stirred up the flames and set to work
mixing her famous tea of dried herbs, ginger, red pepper
and cinnamon, with enough milk added to give the tea a
pleasant color.

Brigham finished his supper and looked at his sons. "You
boys tired?"

"No, Pa, we're not tired."

"Come along, then. We'll take some of your mother's tea
around the camp and ladle it out where it will do the most
good."

Carefully carrying bucketfuls of the steaming concoction,
the trio went about the camp. Some of the Saints had
scraped aside the snow and made tents of their wagon
covers. They were snugly asleep now, so Brigham passed
them by. But there were many others who had little or no
protection against the bitter wind. Women were weeping
with exhaustion, children wailing in misery. When he came
to them, Brigham stopped, doled out hot tea and spoke
encouraging words.

They found a group huddled under a bare bush, a mother
and three children.

"Here, Sister, have a cup of Mother Young's composition
tea!"

The woman gratefully gulped down the warming drink,
her adoring eyes on Brigham's face.

"Where's your husband and wagon?"

The woman shook her head sadly. "We started out with
Brother White and his family. But his wagon broke down,
this side of the bluffs, and they turned back—"

"And you—"

"We walked here. We wanted to go on with you, President Young. On to Zion. We knew you'd get us through somehow. We don't want to be left behind!"

"But your provisions? Food for these children? Way of traveling?"

"We have nothing, President Young. But we want to go on with you."

Brigham could scarcely speak for a moment. What foolhardy people some of the Saints were! But when he spoke his voice was gentle.

"Boys, give the children some composition tea. Then," he added, turning to the mother, "go over to our wagon yonder. Mother Young will feed you and put you to bed for the night. Tomorrow I'll find someone to carry you on."

For hours Brigham and the two boys moved through the camp, giving the hot drink to the women and children. Brigham also took time to visit those of his family who were in the camp, but who were being carried in other wagons. In his own, there was room only for those wives who had children. But in all his care for the thousands around him, he managed never to neglect his own.

When the last of the composition tea had been given out, and the whimpering and crying in the camp was stilled, Brigham laid a hand on his sons' shoulders.

"You are true soldiers," he said approvingly. "Now let us go to bed, too!"

Mary Ann was waiting by the glowing embers she had kept alight to warm her weary husband and sons.

"There are so many to care for!" she sighed. "But you must take care of yourself, too, Brigham. They need you."

Brigham ran his hand worriedly over his face, as if to wipe away the lines of weariness.

"If they would only listen to counsel!" he muttered. "Everything was planned—organized. I wanted to send ahead just a small company of men with small families—

or none at all. They could have found the best route, the
best campsites. They could have built bridges, bought supplies from the Iowa farmers. And the rest could have followed in good order."

"I know, Brigham, but they are afraid to be left behind.
They all want to be right with you."

"And to tell the truth, I am afraid to leave them behind.
I shudder to think what will happen in Nauvoo when the
strength of Israel is gone!"

Brigham had four hours' sleep that night. Early the next
morning he called the Camp of Israel together. In a ringing
voice, he announced the rules of the camp. There weren't
many, but all had to do with keeping law and order among
the people and maintaining sanitary conditions throughout
the campsite.

"We'll have no laws we cannot keep!" he thundered, "but
we will have order in this camp. If anyone wants to live
in peace amongst us he must toe the mark!"

When he dismissed the people, he called Porter Rockwell. "Go back to Nauvoo, Brother Porter, and get Pitts's
Brass Band. Tell the members I want them to come along
now. We must never spend another such dolorous night
as last night!"

Porter mounted his black horse and set out.

They remained at Sugar Creek for two weeks, while
Brigham and Heber and other leaders taught the inexperi-
enced people how to set up tents in a hurry, how to build
campfires and cook over them, how to care for horses and
cattle on the march. And he instilled the principles that
were to govern them: Industry, order, good cheer and real
solicitude for the widows, the aged, the sick and the destitute.

The brass band was a great help. It played martial tunes
during the day as the people struggled along through mud
and rain; it played reverent hymns in the evening when

they gave thanks that they had survived the day's rigors. And when there was time, it played gay dance tunes to liven up long and dreary waits along the march.

The people, straggling across the rain-soaked prairie, wet and cold and hungry, began to sing. There were several poets among them, who composed songs especially suited to their situation. Eliza R. Snow, one of the most noted, composed several stirring hymns, which rang out over the motley caravan, full of hope and courage.

> "Although in woods and tents we dwell,
> Shout! Shout! O Camp of Israel!"

And

> "At the last day-dawn of winter,
> Bound in frost and wrapped in snow;
> Hark! the cry is Onward! Onward!
> Camp of Israel, rise and go!"

And there was a happy favorite:

> "In Upper California, O that's the place for me;
> It lies between the mountains and the great Pacific
> sea.
> The Saints can be protected there and enjoy their
> liberty.
> In Upper California, O that's the place for me!"

Singing and dancing, with the brass band bravely playing, the Saints ignored the cold and snow, the rain and mud, the bitter Iowa winds, and looked ahead to the Zion they would build and enjoy.

Brigham was always busy. Every day new hundreds poured into the camp. Many of them brought little or no provisions for the long, hard journey, even though Brigham had instructed them fully what they should supply. Eight hundred men joined the camp, each one with only two weeks' provisions. Brigham felt desperate, but he would not turn anyone away.

On March 1st he ordered the camp to march on.

"We are too close to Nauvoo," he said. "The brethren keep running back. We must move farther away."

Brigham had not lost sight of his original, careful plan. He still knew he must have the advance parties plant crops for later companies to harvest. He wrote a humble, courteous letter to Governor James Clark of Iowa. He explained why these thousands were traveling across that state, how they had had to abandon their homes and crops. He told how they had been driven away before they could adequately prepare for the journey. He asked permission to plant crops on the public lands and to leave temporary settlements to care for these crops until all his people had been moved from Illinois. The governor never answered the letter, but Brigham Young proceeded to carry out this program. He knew it was the only way to save hundreds from starvation on the prairie.

Brigham Young, watching the long caravan of ill-assorted vehicles, noticed that as each wagon came to the top of a hill the occupants looked back toward Nauvoo, toward the City Beautiful and the gleaming temple they had worked so hard to build. Men's lips drew into hard, bitter lines; women wiped tears from their eyes. This annoyed the leader.

"You look back and weep," he cried. "Why? You don't see Brother Brigham wiping his eyes and sniffling. Do not think that I hate to leave my house and home. Far from that. I am so free from bondage at this time that Nauvoo looks like a prison to me. It looks pleasant ahead, but dark to look back!"

Brigham sent Parley P. Pratt ahead with a small group to search out the best camping places, to build bridges or locate fords. And slowly, sometimes three or four miles a day, sometimes only one mile, the caravan of three thousand men, women and children moved across the muddy Iowa land.

They reached the Chariton River by the end of March. It had taken them a month to travel one hundred miles.

By now Brigham had thoroughly organized the entire moving mass. It was divided into companies of hundreds, fifties, tens, with a captain over each. The men were ordered to walk beside their teams or wagons, their guns loaded and in their hands or within easy reach. Every male over twelve was to have a gun. At night the wagons were to be drawn into a closed circle, with the teams and cattle tethered inside this enclosure.

Brigham appointed "bosses" for each activity of the camp—a boss of the commissary, a boss of the hunters, a boss of lost articles, a boss of exploration.

"And Brigham to boss himself and all the other bosses!" he said, chuckling. The people chuckled, too. They knew well how necessary this one boss was.

Each morning at five the bugle awakened the camp. The people arose and attended to prayers before leaving their wagons. "It would be a sad thing," Brigham said, "for this people to go into the mountains and forget their God."

The women prepared breakfast while the men fed the animals. After breakfast the women cleared away and packed their things, while the men hitched up the teams. At seven another bugle call started the day's march.

Camp was made at five in the afternoon, or as near that time as a good site was found. When the last bugle blew at nine, all were in bed.

On the Grand River, one hundred and fifty miles from Nauvoo, they stopped to plant corn and wheat. Here they left their first way station, calling it Garden Grove. A few families remained there to look after the crops.

On the middle fork of the Grand River they planted another way station. They named this one Mount Pisgah. And on June 14th they reached the Indian agency at Council Bluffs on the Missouri River.

Brigham called Heber and the other apostles to council.

"It has taken us four months to cross Iowa," he said. "Our teams and cattle are starving. Our provisions are gone. It is too late in the year to start toward the mountains. We must stop here for a time."

His companions agreed. "We can build a settlement here," Brigham went on, "which can serve as a last stopping place for all who plan to go to the mountains. We can build a good, stout ferryboat, plant crops. And next spring we can leave for Zion!"

"How many wagons are behind us on the trail now?" Orson Hyde asked.

"About nine hundred. Already here or on the road are around fifteen thousand people. We must build a place for them to stop."

Before Brigham had time to make much of a start on the new settlement, however, there was sudden excitement in the camp.

Captain James Allen of the United States Army came galloping up with a small detachment of soldiers. Women, seeing the troops and remembering what the militia in Missouri had done, gathered their children and ran to hide.

"We're at war with Mexico!" Captain Allen announced. "President Polk wants you to fit out a battalion of five hundred volunteers to march to California and help take over that country!"

Mutters of protest rose from the men who had gathered to hear what the soldiers wanted. "The United States drives us out and then asks us to fight its battles!" "What do we care about war with Mexico? We may have to go to Mexico ourselves to find peace!" "What did the President do for us when Brigham Young asked for protection?"

But Brigham's eyes narrowed shrewdly. There were always two sides to a bargain if you were smart.

He could understand the President's maneuver. Here were strong, obedient men, already well on the way west. The country was at war with Mexico. Britain was trying to claim Oregon. If the Saints reached the Pacific coast and joined either of these two enemies, they could give the United States a difficult time of it. It would be better by far to win them over, have them on the side of the United States troops.

Brigham's lips quirked in his humorous smile. Well, two could play the game of self-interest! This could be a bit of good luck for the Saints.

He held up his hand to stop the growing threat in the sullen voices.

"Captain Allen!" he said clearly. Everyone stood still. Brigham would put that presumptuous soldier in his place! This would be worth hearing.

"Captain Allen, you shall have your men. If the young men won't go, we'll take the old men. And if they refuse, we'll make up a company of women. You shall have your battalion, sir!"

CHAPTER ELEVEN

OVERNIGHT—A TOWN!

→»-→»-→»-→»-→»-→»-→»-→»-→»-→»

For the next two weeks Brigham was busy recruiting volunteers for the Mormon Battalion. Up and down the long line of moving wagons he rode. He stopped at every camp and urged the young and able-bodied to join Captain Allen.

At first, everywhere the response was the same as it was at Mount Pisgah where Willard Richards was in charge. When the people of this way station had first seen Captain Allen and his men approaching, a cry of dismay had gone up. "The troops are upon us!" Terrified, remembering Missouri, parents gathered their children close and watched the soldiers come.

Now their beloved leader stood among them asking them to join the soldiers, to leave their families here on the frontier and march away to fight!

"It's a trick! They just want to get the menfolk away so the Indians can kill our women and children!"

"No, Brother," Brigham answered patiently. "For once the government is offering us something that will help us. It's the first time we've had any help from the government; let's take it."

"Help? How can it help us to send our men away?"

"Don't you see? These five hundred men will be transported to the coast—and paid while they go. Not only will they be paid cash that their families can use, but given food and clothing as well. Better still, those men, those

Mormon men, will be among the first to get into that country. Think what that means! I don't want anyone to be there ahead of us and think they have the right to drive us out when we come. I could wish we had got there before this! But since we couldn't we must be among the very first!"

The listeners thought this over. Brother Brigham was right, as usual. He thought of every angle to a situation. Trust him to turn a bad bargain into a good one!

"But our families?"

"I promise you I'll do my best to see that your families are brought forward with the rest. They shall have food as long as I myself have anything to eat. If we do this, if we answer the government's call for help, that same government will be bound to help us when we cry out. But it's up to you, Brethren. I have Captain Allen's promise that we can remain here without any trouble as long as we find it necessary to tarry. I can counsel you. I can tell you what is best for you and for us all. It's up to you whether you listen to that counsel and act upon it."

The men whispered and muttered and considered.

"We'd get forty-two dollars a year clothing allowance. That would help my family a lot. I don't know when I've seen forty-two dollars at one time in the past years," someone pointed out.

"And we get paid every month—in hard cash! I'm going!"

Brigham, Heber and Willard Richards rode back to their camp. Behind them came the volunteers.

At his home in the camp, Brigham found a stranger waiting for him. He was a fine-looking man, with a wide brow, deep-set eyes, curling dark hair and beard. He held out his hand.

"President Young? I am Colonel Thomas E. Kane. I was to meet Captain Allen here."

The two men stood for a moment, measuring each other. Almost simultaneously they smiled. Brigham took the outstretched hand, and a permanent friendship was sealed by the act.

"Captain Allen is here, Colonel Kane. We've been out recruiting your men."

"Will you be able to raise the battalion?"

"Certainly, sir! I've never yet called on the Saints that they haven't responded. Just wait a day or two and you'll see. And now, are you comfortably lodged, sir?"

Colonel Kane nodded. "I am amazed at your city, President Young. I must call it a city! A year ago there was nothing here—and now a teeming, bustling community."

"We haven't had time yet to do much. We had scarcely arrived when Captain Allen came. But if you're here a few months—or even weeks—you'll see what the Saints can do when they put their minds to it."

Three days after this conversation, the Stars and Stripes was run to the top of a slender tree, stripped of its branches to make a flagpole. The bugle sounded. The excited people gathered in the bowery. This was a shelter of poles and branches which the Saints had learned how to erect in a very short time to give them a place to hold their religious services and public gatherings and entertainments.

They came today dressed in their best, for this was to be a farewell party for the men of the battalion. The women wore dresses of lawn or gingham or calico, washed and starched. Their white petticoats and carefully darned white stockings gave no hint that they had been washed in the river and dried upon willows. The men's clothes, too, were cleaned and brushed as carefully as if their wearers were attending a ball at the finest hotel.

Only one thing was lacking. Colonel Kane looked questioningly at his host.

"I notice, President Young, that your people do not wear jewelry. Is that one of the tenets of your faith—the ban on jewelry?"

Brigham smiled wryly. "No, sir. We don't believe in any sort of ostentation, but a good piece of jewelry is certainly permissible. These people have owned such things. Look at the ladies' ears, sir. You'll see they have been pierced for earrings. And the men's waistcoats have watch pockets. They are empty because the owners sold everything they could part with to obtain provisions for our journey to the mountains."

Now Duzett's Military Band and Pitts's Brass Band united in such a stirring military air that the very trees seemed to tremble with excitement. Laggards hastened their steps. Everyone hurried toward the bowery.

When the strains of the first cotillion rang out, Brigham bowed to Mary Ann and led her out onto the hard-packed earth of the bowery floor. Colonel Kane, courtly and charming, chose a partner; Heber Kimball, Willard Richards and the other elders joined them. Soon the bowery was filled with dancing, swaying figures. Outside of the shelter, others found room to join in. Even the children chose their partners and danced gaily.

During a pause, Colonel Kane found himself again beside Brigham.

"I am amazed, sir, at your people. There is no weeping and wailing. This is joy, sheer happiness, and yet it is a farewell ball. These men are going off to war—"

"I have promised them, sir, that not one shall die in battle."

The officer's eyes opened in astonishment. "You can do that? With assurance?"

Brigham's lips quirked in one of his rare, humorous smiles. "I can, sir, and I have." Then he went on more soberly, "I have always believed that music and happiness are necessary, especially when people are troubled, or seem to have little to rejoice over. I encourage the Saints to sing and to dance. This has sustained us many times."

The next morning the battalion marched away behind Captain Allen. There were some tears then, of course, and some sad faces. Women clung to their husbands or sons; children cried out for their fathers. But the band played, the flags waved and the men marched proudly. The few women who were going along as cooks and laundresses rode in light carriages behind the marching column.

As soon as they were out of sight, Brigham Young said, "Now I can get about the work of this camp!"

Colonel Kane did not march away with the battalion. He was feeling ill and had decided to rest here a few days and then overtake the troops. But he grew worse instead of better, and it was many a long day before he could leave the settlement. For a time, the good women who nursed him almost despaired of saving the officer's life. But they worked and prayed over him, caring for him as tenderly as if he had been one of their own. And finally he recovered.

Brigham took stock of what had been done toward making a settlement here on the banks of the Missouri. The tents and wagons were scattered helter-skelter along the river bottoms. The people were again ailing with chills and fever.

"Heber," Brigham said to his companion, "we must find a better location than this. Get your horse. Let's take a look along the river."

The two friends rode together along the bluffs above the Missouri, searching for a suitable site for a semipermanent settlement.

"We don't know how many years we'll have to use this place," Brigham observed. "There are some twenty thousand people on the move behind us, or already here. And after we go on to the mountains, there will be thousands more coming from the foreign missions. We should consider all this."

He drew rein and pointed across the river. "There, on that

western bank is a beautiful site. There are trees for building houses and for fuel, a stream coming down to the river, plenty of room for our cabins. And behind that, the prairie for pasture."

"It belongs to the Omaha Nation," Heber pointed out. "Here, we are on Potawatomie land."

"We'll ask permission to locate there. Big Elk is the Omaha chieftain, isn't he? I'll send him a letter."

Heber smiled, his black eyes merry. "Do you think he can read it?"

"He has people who can do so, I'm sure. In the meantime, we'll send some surveyors over there to see whether I am right in choosing that place. They can judge whether a settlement can profitably be laid out there."

"Didn't Captain Allen tell you that we could stay here if we'd send the battalion?"

"Yes, and I plan to do so. But I will also ask Big Elk's permission. It is best to keep on friendly terms with the Indians."

He addressed his letter courteously to the Omaha chieftain, calling him "Brother" and explaining what the Mormons wished to do.

"Have you any objections to our getting timber, building houses and staying here until spring or longer? The government is willing, if you are. Would you like to have some of our mechanics repair your guns? Are you disposed to be on amicable terms with us? I will be glad to have you express yourselves freely on these subjects."

This was something new to Big Elk. Always before, the white man had taken what he wanted, without so much as a by-your-leave. Big Elk thought about the matter.

The Omahas at this time were in an unhappy situation. Smallpox had reduced them from a powerful nation to a mere handful of proud, but almost helpless, people. They were at the mercy of the warlike Sioux, who rode down upon them, killing them when they tried to harvest their corn or hunt wild game for their families. It would be a good thing to have an ally near, to have their guns repaired, to be able to obtain balls and powder.

He sent word back to Brigham Young:

> My son, thou hast spoken well. I have all thou hast said in my heart. I have much I want to say. We are poor. When we go to hunt game in one place, we meet an enemy, and so in another place our enemies kill us. We do not kill them. I hope we will be friends. You may stay on these lands two years or more. Our young men may watch your cattle. We would be glad to have you trade with us. We will warn you of danger from other Indians.

With this assurance, Brigham and his people set to work. Surveyors laid out a regular townsite. Lots were apportioned to families. Log cabins went up with amazing rapidity. A council house was built and also schoolhouses. The settlement, called simply "Winter Quarters," was divided into "wards," with a bishop over each.

Everyone worked. The children herded the cattle and sheep and carried wood and water. The women did all the household chores and carded, spun and knit. The men built the settlement.

When at last Colonel Kane was able to walk about, Brigham came to take him on a tour of the new town. The colonel stared about him, unbelievingly.

"What has happened here?" he exclaimed. "A city has appeared while I lay helpless!"

Brigham chuckled, pleased. "I told you I would show you what the Saints can do."

"But this is really a city—streets and houses and public buildings mushrooming overnight! Is that a schoolhouse?"

"Yes, we have schools. We can't let our children welter in ignorance. Our Prophet once said, 'The glory of God is intelligence.'"

"I can't believe it!" the officer muttered. "And these are the people Missouri drove out. These are the people Illinois would not have!" He turned to Brigham and tears were in his eyes. "You know, sir, I owe my life to your people. Not in the finest cities could I have received better care. I want you to know that I appreciate it, sir. And if ever your people need a friend in the East, I want you to call upon me."

Brigham's lips twitched wryly. "I'll remember, Colonel. We'll likely need friends. We've *always* needed 'em!"

CHAPTER TWELVE

TO SEEK A NEW ZION

➤➤➤-➤➤➤-➤➤➤-➤➤➤-➤➤➤-➤➤➤-➤➤➤-➤➤➤-➤➤➤-➤➤➤

Late in August Colonel Kane was well enough to leave Winter Quarters for the East. Soon word came back from him concerning what he had found when he reached Nauvoo.

He had arrived at the Mississippi settlement only to find that once beautiful and prosperous city turned into a dead and desolate place. Houses were standing in ruins, their empty window frames staring out unhappily at the empty streets. The gardens that had been the pride and joy of the Saints lay trampled and abandoned. Ripe corn and wheat stood unharvested in the fields.

The officer went up from the river into the city and found groups of ruffians "standing guard" over the town.

"We druv them Mormons out!" one of them boasted gleefully. "Regular battle we had, an' we won, dog blast it! The Battle of Nauvoo!"

These ruffians had taken possession of the beautiful temple, desecrating it in every conceivable manner.

"But where are they—the ones you drove away?" Kane asked.

The fellows winked. "How do we know. Mebbe, ef yore plumb set on findin' 'em, you might go look in them there willows t'other side of the river."

Colonel Kane hurried across to the western bank of the Mississippi and there he found them. The only Saints that had remained in Nauvoo were those who were too sick or too old to travel, or who had not yet been able to provide even the barest essentials for the journey west. Now this unhappy remnant was hiding among the willows along the riverbank. The sick and old and dying lay on the ground, unprotected from the daytime sun or the cold of the September night.

A terrible anger surged up in Colonel Kane. He remembered the Mormon women who had cared so tenderly for him when he was ill, and he went among the stricken Saints doing what he could for their comfort. One of his first acts was to send a messenger posthaste to Brigham with word of the disaster.

When Brigham received the message, his face flushed with anger; his blue eyes flashed.

"Get relief teams and wagons ready at once!" he ordered. "We must send back for those people!"

Some grumbled. "We've got plenty to do here! That's a long, hard trip back! What if we're murdered when we get there?"

Brigham answered sternly, "Have you forgotten our covenant? We made it at Far West and again at Nauvoo. But if you've forgotten, I will refresh your memory. We took a solemn oath that we would stand by each other, assist each other to the utmost, and that we would never desert the poor and the worthy. I hope never to see the day when the thought of our own safety or comfort holds us back from helping those who are less fortunate than we."

He looked at the grumblers, his mouth grim. "Now, hitch up your wagons and go back to Nauvoo. And let me hear no more complaining."

Back the wagons went. By winter nearly every Mormon had been brought out of Illinois to Winter Quarters or one of the way stations. The only ones remaining in the aban-

doned city were a few who still had property they wished
to hold onto, or who were trying to protect church property.

In November a stranger came into Winter Quarters from
the West. Brigham heard that Father de Smet, a Catholic
missionary, was in the village, and he invited the traveler
to visit him.

The two men liked each other immediately. Each could
see that the other was a man of integrity and unselfish
purpose.

"You have been in the West for many years, they tell me,"
Brigham began. "I'd like to learn all I can about it, because
we want to go out there."

Father de Smet smiled. "That's what your people tell me.
Well, I think I can answer any questions you may have.
You'll find some good land and some bad; some wonderful
areas and some desolate ones."

"There has been some thought of Vancouver Island. I
have sent men to make inquiries about that place and the
possibility of our making a settlement there."

"That is beautiful, rich country," the missionary answered.
"Already some missionaries have made settlements near by
in Oregon country."

Brigham frowned. "I don't want to go where there are
other settlements. You will understand, sir, that we have
not been treated well by our neighbors in the past. We'd
like to go where we would have no neighbors. What about
the Great Basin? I have here the maps and reports of Captain John C. Frémont. One of our missionaries brought them
back from Washington, where they were published last
year."

He spread a map on the table. It showed the Rocky Mountains and the Sierra Nevadas and the Pacific coast line. Between the two mountain ranges was a great, empty space,
with the Great Salt Lake at the eastern border. Brigham
put his hand upon this space.

"This great basin, here. It looks as if there were no settlements in the whole area."

"There are none that I know of," Father de Smet agreed, "and for a good reason. That is all desert country. Even the Indians have difficulty finding a living. They dig in the sand for roots, and so have been called Digger Indians. They eat crickets and ants and any small vermin. Anything as large as a rabbit is scarce. I'm afraid that your people could not easily exist in that country. Although, of course," the missionary smiled suddenly, "it is surprising what a people can do if they are sustained by faith and by hope."

Brigham Young's frown disappeared and his eyes were sunny. He extended his hand. "That's my belief in a nutshell. Thank you, Father."

That winter was a busy one. There were now twelve thousand people in Winter Quarters alone. And every one of these was working toward the journey westward in the spring. It was the feverish activity of Nauvoo all over again. But there was recreation, also, and always the religious services and the strict observance of the Sabbath day.

If any one had a moment's time, it was put into making things to sell in the neighboring Missouri communities or to the Indians. The women wove willow baskets and the men made wooden washboards, which could be sold for cash or traded for flour, sugar, salt or skins.

Brigham told Heber, "There's not an hour of the day or night when I can't hear the ax or the hammer or the saw."

Heber's black eyes twinkled. "Or the fiddle, Brother Brigham! Or the brass band!"

"Well, they are a good people. They work hard. They must have some pleasure. You know, Heber, I'm a great believer in suitable recreation. Work and faith and happiness. Those three things can accomplish miracles."

Heber agreed. "But I don't see how you keep going. You

sleep with one eye open and one foot out of bed. When anything is wanted, there you are, right on hand."

"And you with me. You and the rest of the Twelve. We are all in harmony—and that's a great thing for the good of the church."

"The supplies for the exodus are coming in very well," Heber went on. "But I've heard that one brother has eaten his seed corn."

Brigham showed impatience. "They must not do that! I wish they had to pay three dollars a bushel for their seed corn. Then they wouldn't be so fast to consume it. We must have three hundred bushels or more to take with us in the first company."

"Have you decided where we are to go?"

"I'm calling a meeting of the Twelve to discuss that. I've received some new maps from St. Louis showing all the Indian country. We'll look them over and discuss the problem. I want to be ready to start right after the April conference."

Heber remarked thoughtfully, "The conference idea was one of Joseph's greatest inspirations, I think. Meeting like that—calling all the Saints together twice a year does a lot toward holding us together. The faith of the people is renewed—"

"And our faith, too!" Brigham added. "I always feel a sweet spirit at those gatherings."

The council met and discussed plans for the move to the mountains. A small, select company would leave in April. This would consist of one hundred and forty-four men. They would go ahead, mark the route, find fords and camp-sites. And they would find the site of the new Zion somewhere in that vast western country. Other companies would follow in orderly sequence throughout the spring.

The Twelve studied the maps from St. Louis and those drawn by Captain Frémont. They discussed the various proposed goals—Oregon, Vancouver Island, California, Texas, Mexico.

"I still favor the basin of the Great Salt Lake," Brigham said at last. "The Prophet Joseph said to take the Saints to the Rocky Mountains. I believe that once we get away from people and put our thoughts and hands to work for the Lord, we'll be happier than we have ever been."

At the general conference on April 6th, the seventeenth anniversary of the organization of the church, Brigham told the Saints that everything was in readiness for the first party to set out. Some of the selected men had already left and were waiting on the Elkhorn River for the rest to come. The people looked at their leader and fear was in their hearts.

"What shall we do when you are gone?" they asked. "What if mobs come against us again?"

"If mob violence should render it necessary for all to move," Brigham answered sturdily, "take your cows, put your loads on their backs, fasten your children on top and set out. If you do all you can, the Lord will do the rest."

"Why can't we all go with you?"

"That is impossible. We don't know what we'll find along the way—whether there will be food and forage and water for us. We are not going to expose this people to starvation and death on the prairie. And we don't know where we'll stop. No, I don't want the confusion and misery we suffered coming to this place from Nauvoo. I want everything carried out in order. I can see clearly that if you will all follow my counsel, I can transport you to Zion and we will rejoice there together."

The people murmured. He was right. He was always right.

"And now," he went on, "do not be afraid. As for me, I feel like a father with a great family of children around me in a winter storm. I am looking with calmness and patience for the clouds to break and the sun to shine. Have faith—

do your part and I will soon gather you around me again in the new Zion!"

His words comforted the people. He spoke straight to their hearts. Brigham had had only eleven days of formal schooling in all his boyhood. He was no orator such as the preachers whom he had heard in his youth. He never yelled and gestured. But he spoke clearly and forcibly, in language his listeners could understand—the words of the Bible and of the farm intermingled. When he quoted the Bible or the Book of Mormon it was in short, pithy passages, not long parables. He talked to the people as if he were an elder brother or a father. And, in fact, the Saints had come to look upon him rather as a beloved father than anything else—one to whom they could take even their smallest troubles and be sure of help.

The next day Brigham made ready to join the others on the Elkhorn. His original party of one hundred and forty-four men had been somewhat modified. One of the men was too ill to make the trip, and three women had been added to the company. Brigham hadn't planned to take any women on this first expedition, but Heber Kimball was not well and needed specially prepared food. Yet he would not stay behind and Brigham did not want his best friend to miss this historic trip.

"Take one of your wives along to care for you, Heber," Brigham advised.

Heber's eyes twinkled. "Just one woman will be mighty lonesome all by herself."

Brigham's quick smile answered. "Well, I can take Clara, if you take Ellen. They are good friends. And then my brother Lorenzo can take Harriet. She's Clara's mother and can look after the two younger women. How will that be? But I don't want more than three—they'll be enough to be responsible for."

This worked out very well, and the only other change made was in permitting two boys to accompany the party.

There were seventy-two carriages and wagons, and also oxen, horses, cattle, sheep and chickens. The party carried seed corn and seed potatoes, wheat and buckwheat. They took farming, blacksmithing and manufacturing tools and scientific instruments.

Just as they were ready to leave, Parley P. Pratt arrived from England with the very best astronomical instruments he had been able to procure. His brother Orson, the best mathematician in the church at this time, was overjoyed. Now the route could be accurately mapped and a record of latitude, longitude and altitude could be kept.

On the morning of April 7th, all the Saints of the whole area—those in Winter Quarters and those in smaller settlements along the river—gathered to bid their leader Godspeed.

The evening before, Brigham had visited every member of his large family and had given them careful instructions. Mary Ann was to stay in Winter Quarters until the following summer.

Brigham, looking fondly at the patient, kind face, lifting a lock of the dark hair that had strayed across her cheek and smoothing it gently back, said, "I shall be less worried knowing you are here to look after things. Winter Quarters will be a poor place when Mother Young leaves it." He kissed her tenderly, then turned to the children, seven of them now, crowding around him.

"Take care of your mother, Joseph. You stand in my place when I am gone." He kissed each of them, promising to remember them all in his prayers. "And I'll be back in the autumn. You can count on that!"

Lucy Decker, Clara's older sister, was also to stay over until the next year; but some of the wives and children were to come out with the second company under Parley P. Pratt and some in the third company, to be led by John Taylor. The latter would leave later that same summer and follow the trail marked out by Brigham's group.

Now, on this April morning, Brigham, Heber, Orson Pratt and Willard Richards, together with their companions, drew their wagons into formation. The command was given and the train began to move. Slowly it wound down the dusty road and into the unknown West.

Brigham looked back and lifted his hand in a familiar gesture of farewell. The band struck up a tune and on the clear air thousands of voices rose:

> "Though deepening trials throng your way,
> Press on! Press on, ye Saints of God!
> Ere long the Resurrection Day
> Will spread its light and life abroad.
> Lift up your hearts in praise to God;
> Let your rejoicings never cease—"

Above the rumbling of the wagons, the words rang out until the caravan had passed from sight.

CHAPTER THIRTEEN

ACROSS THE WIDE LAND

>>>->>>->>>->>>->>>->>>->>>->>>->>>->>>

At dark on the night of April 9th, the caravan made camp on the open prairie. Brigham Young and the other apostles in the train went out with the teamsters to cut the long prairie grass for their animals. As he swung the sharp-edged scythe, Brigham remembered his boyhood days in Sherburne.

"We've come a long way from our childhood, Heber," he remarked.

Heber paused and straightened up. "And we're just at the beginning!"

"Yes. This is the beginning, really. I am confident of that," Brigham agreed.

They fed their teams, ate their own supper, then retired to the wagon Brigham had fitted up as a comfortable bedroom for him and Heber to use on the long trek.

Brigham had issued strict orders concerning this march, as he had done for the journey from Nauvoo to the Missouri River. This camp was also divided into companies and had captains and supervisors for every aspect of the journey. The hours of marching, the form of encampment and all such details had proved so workable on the former journey that they were adopted for this much longer trip.

Special duties were assigned to the men best fitted for them. Orson Pratt, the scientist, was to make careful astronomical and geographical observations. Dr. Willard Richards, with his superior education, was to be camp his-

torian. Porter Rockwell, the expert marksman, was in charge
of the hunters. Thomas Tanner was in charge of the small
cannon Brigham had brought along as protection against the
Indians, while Brigham and Heber planned to ride at the
head of the caravan and pick out the route.

One of the busiest men in the train was William Clayton,
camp clerk, musician and poet. This careful little English-
man with his well-cut, expensive clothing, his plump white
hands and his love of order and detail, found many tasks
put upon his willing shoulders. One of these was to record
the distance traveled each day, and to see that markers were
left along the route to guide later emigration trains.

Keeping an accurate record of the distance traveled was,
at first, a real problem. At nightfall each of the men had a
different estimate of the number of miles they had covered.

"What shall I do, Brother Brigham?" Clayton asked. "I
do want to have an accurate measurement."

Brigham frowned thoughtfully. "You could fasten a chain
to a wheel and count the revolutions the wheel makes.
Multiply that by the wheel's circumference and you'd know
exactly how far you'd traveled."

Clayton sighed. It would be dreadfully monotonous to
count every revolution of a wagon wheel! But since he could
think of nothing better just then, he fastened a strip of
bright red flannel to a wheel spoke and walked along beside
the wagon, counting.

Each time the flannel strip came to the top of the wheel,
the careful watcher noted it. Mile after mile he trudged
along. He had measured the wheel and found that it would
make just three hundred and sixty revolutions to a mile.
Now as he walked beside the wheel, with the dust coming
up into his eyes and nose and mouth, he muttered, "One
hundred twenty, one hundred and twenty-one—one thousand seventeen—eighteen hundred and two" and so on, all
day long.

But William Clayton's mind was not going around and around with the wheel. His thoughts were darting here and there, trying to find a solution—some method that would relieve him of this deadly monotony. After a couple of days, he took Orson Pratt aside one evening when camp had been made.

"Brother Orson," he began at once, "I believe we could make a simple piece of machinery that would do this counting for us. All we'd need are some wooden cogwheels that Appleton Harmon, the carpenter, can make. I figured it out like this—"

Carefully he explained the mechanism which could be fitted onto the wagon wheel to record the revolutions.

Orson Pratt nodded. "Yes, Brother William. That would work all right. We'll have it constructed at once."

Clayton called his contraption an odometer and was very proud of it. Now he was free to play in the band and compose songs for them to sing along the way. He was very good at this. He could take almost any event or situation and fashion a hymn to suit the occasion. One of his hymns became the favorite of the emigrants, and whenever the way became particularly desperate or when an accident or death made the journey seem too difficult to bear, this song would break out somewhere along the long line, and soon, all would be singing.

"Come, come ye Saints, no toil or labor fear,
But with joy, wend your way.
Though hard to you this journey may appear,
Grace shall be as your day.
'Tis better far for us to strive
Our useless cares from us to drive.
Do this and joy your hearts will swell.
All is well! All is well!"

At night on the prairie, after supper had been eaten, the Saints would gather around the campfires to pray and sing and dance. Brigham told his people: "The world considers it very wicked for a Christian to hear music and to dance. Many preachers say that fiddling and music come from hell. But I say there is no fiddling, no music in hell. Music belongs to heaven, to cheer God, angels and men. Music and dancing are for the benefit of holy ones, and all who come here to-night who are not holy and righteous and do not worship God have no right to be here."

The band would strike up a gay quadrille and Brigham would lead out as he had done at Winter Quarters and at Nauvoo—a gallant figure, stepping lightly and happily to the lively tune.

Brigham had decided that the company should travel along the north bank of the Platte River. On the southern bank there was already a well-marked road over which hundreds of wagons had moved and were moving toward the Oregon country.

"I don't want to run into any of those people!" Brigham said decidedly. "Many are Missourians and all start out from Missouri. So they have the curse of that people upon them. The States have driven us out—they don't want anything to do with us—and I can tell you, Brethren, I feel the same toward them. We'll make our own road!"

Porter Rockwell nodded. "An' we'll have more chance at game along here where no one else is travelin'!" he remarked.

Two weeks after leaving Winter Quarters, the caravan came in sight of a Pawnee village. Having been warned that these Indians had been stirred up against the Mormons, Brigham fully expected some trouble when Chief Shefmolun and his troop of braves came into the camp.

The chieftain proved friendly, however, and after Brigham and some of the others made presents to the Indians, giving them flour and tobacco and salt, they went away and left the Saints alone. Brigham set extra guards that night, in order to make sure the camp was not taken by surprise. He himself took his turn along with the regular guard.

A week later, the travelers saw their first buffalo. William Clayton was looking through his spyglass when he saw a moving brown mass. Before he could tell the others, a sound like the low rumbling of thunder was heard. Then hundreds of the huge, shaggy creatures came pounding across the prairie, their heads down, their great shoulders hunched, a cloud of dust rising over them.

"Buffalo!" Porter Rockwell yelled delightedly. "Git yore guns, men, and after them!"

Excitement surged through the camp. The men, forgetting Brigham's orders not to leave their posts, leaped onto horses and went galloping away toward the rushing brown herd. Shots rang out. Porter, coming face to face with a huge bull, aimed point-blank between the eyes and fired. The animal did not pause but galloped on, seemingly unaware that he had been hit.

"I'll be doggoned!" Porter muttered. "That hair's so thick on his forehead a bullet can't git through it!"

Bang! bang! bang! bang! The guns barked merrily. When the herd galloped past, Porter's hunters found they had killed one bull and three cows. Porter galloped back to report to his leader.

"Plenty of fresh meat, Brother Brigham! Kin we have some wagons to bring it in?"

Camp was made at the next good spot. The buffalo was dressed and apportioned out. They cut chunks of the rich meat and roasted them on long sticks over the glowing campfires, then ate till they could eat no more.

Brigham walked among the feasting companies, observing everything. The next morning he called his people together.

"We must not kill any more game than we need at the

time," he said sternly. "Remember, if we slay when we do not need, we shall certainly need when we cannot slay!"

They met a group of Mountain Men led by Charles Beaumont, taking their winter's catch of peltries down to St. Louis. Brigham asked him about the western regions and then said, "Will you carry letters back to the frontier for us?"

Beaumont's bearded lips parted in a smile. "Certainly, m'sieu. Prepare them."

There was a great flurry of letter writing in camp that afternoon. When Beaumont went on, he carried a fat package of letters.

One by one they passed famous landmarks. The camp was generally well behaved, but if the singing and merrymaking became too boisterous, Brigham did not hesitate to reprove the transgressors.

"Cease your folly and turn to the Lord!" he advised them sternly. "I will not have disorder in this camp. Before long there will be arguments, then knives will be drawn; and the next thing will be bloodshed. I will have an orderly camp or I will get rid of the troublemakers!"

On June 1st, Brigham's forty-sixth birthday, the train reached Fort Laramie.

"We are exactly 543¼ miles from Winter Quarters!" William Clayton announced triumphantly, reading his odometer.

At Fort Laramie the company was joined by a small party of Mississippi Saints. These people had left Mississippi the previous year, about the time Nauvoo had been vacated. They had expected to meet the Nauvoo Saints at Fort Laramie and go on with them. But when the Saints had been held up at Winter Quarters, the Mississippi group had wintered at Pueblo. Now, leaving most of the company at Pueblo, a few had pushed on and they rejoiced to meet their friends. And they brought news of the Mormon Battalion men.

Some of them had been ill and had been sent to Pueblo to recuperate.

"Looks like the hand of God was directing us," said Robert Crow, leader of the little band of seventeen men, women and children. "We were there to care for those boys when they came in sick."

"How had they fared—our battalion boys?" Brigham asked.

"Not too well. Mebbe you'd better hear the battalion song —that tells the whole story." And without waiting for an invitation, he began:

> Our hardships reached their rough extremes
> When valiant men were roped with teams
> Hour after hour and day after day
> To wear our strength and lives away.
> How hard to starve and wear us out
> Upon this sandy, desert route!

The song went on for verse after verse, telling of the hardships of the boys. When at last he came to the end, Crow rubbed his chin and said quizzically, "They've gone on to Californy now, and will be comin' up acrost the mountings to meet us when we reach Zion."

James Bordeaux, the owner of Fort Laramie, which was really a trading post rather than a fort, told Brigham, "I've heard all sorts of bad things about you Mormons, but I can say this—you're by far the best-behaved company that has come this way since I've been here."

Four men rode into the fort and said they were on their way from St. Joseph, Missouri, to Oregon.

"We've passed two thousand wagons on the road—all bent for the Oregon country. So we cut loose and are getting ahead as fast as we can. We don't aim to be the last ones there!"

Brigham turned to Heber. "California and Oregon are going to be crowded. I hope we can find some place where we'll be first!"

On the Platte River, the caravan ran into difficulty. They had a "bull boat"—a boat made of hides stretched over a frame—to carry their goods across the river. But the current was too swift for the teams, so rafts had to be constructed and the wagons taken across on these. While the Mormons were busy at this work, a train of Oregon-bound Missourians came along. They begged the Mormons to raft them across.

"All right," Brigham agreed. "Carry them across for one dollar and fifty cents or two dollars a load, according to its size. They can pay in cash, or in goods at St. Louis prices."

When the job was done, the Saints looked with satisfaction at the results. They had collected nearly thirteen hundred pounds of flour, as well as meal and beans, honey, soap and cloth.

"This gives me an idea," the practical-minded Brigham observed. "We'll leave some men here with these rafts. They can collect ferriage from those two thousand wagons that are on the road. What they get will be welcomed by the later companies of Saints. And if there is more than those companies need, they can bring it on with them."

Volunteers were called for to remain at the Platte River ferry and ten were selected for this job. The others bade their friends farewell and moved on toward the famous South Pass, by which they could take wagons over the Continental Divide.

CHAPTER FOURTEEN

THIS IS THE PLACE

➤➤-➤➤-➤➤-➤➤-➤➤-➤➤-➤➤-➤➤-➤➤

Orson Pratt was excited as the caravan neared South Pass.

"I must make calculations there," he said eagerly. "If this pass hadn't been discovered, we might have found it impossible to take wagons to the Rocky Mountains."

Brigham agreed. "Captain Frémont made his first trip out here in '42. His report on what he found was published the following year. I've read it. I was struck by what he said—that the pass is not the narrow, rocky defile one might expect, but a slow, gentle slope over which wagons can pass with great ease."

Before they reached the pass, however, a famous Mountain Man came into camp. This was old Black Harris, now dignified by the title—acquired goodness knows where—of major.

"Yore men's been askin' about the South Pass," Major Harris said to Brigham. "Wah! I'm the child kin tell ye about that thar place. I wuz with old Jed Smith in '24 when he found that way acrost the mountings. I wuz jest plain old Black Harris then—biggest liar in the mountings!" he added proudly. Then, wistfully, "Old Gabe Bridger has stole thet honor frum me, I reckon!"

Brigham shook the great hairy paw and gazed deeply into the black eyes nearly hidden beneath the bushy, unkempt hair and beard. In spite of his coarse language, the constant spitting of tobacco juice and his boast about being such a great liar, Brigham felt that here was a man that could be trusted.

"We'd like to find out whether a colony could exist on the shores of the Great Salt Lake," Brigham explained. "We can find the South Pass, I'm sure. But we don't know much about the Great Basin."

"Wal, now, thar's better places, I kin tell ye. Wah! Even the Injuns hev a hard time makin' a livin' thar. This child'll tell ye, thet country ain't got enough trees to build cabins fer a hundert folks. Don't this child know, though? I wuz one of old Jed's Great Salt Lake Men—fust band to make camp in thet thar country. Wah!"

Brigham frowned thoughtfully. "That's the report I get from almost everyone. And yet—I feel sure that is where we should go."

Major Harris went on with the party he was guiding. Since the trapping business was no longer the profitable occupation it had been twenty years before, he, like many of his friends, had taken to guiding emigrant trains across the prairies and mountains.

A few days later, Brigham heard that another of these old-timers was at hand.

Porter Rockwell reported. "Brother Brigham," he said, "I jest been talkin' to Jim Bridger. He has a post on the Green River, about two hundred miles north of the Great Salt Lake. He sez he wuz the first white man to lay eyes on the lake. He's camped down the road a piece."

"Bring him to me," Brigham ordered. He was eager to see this famous Mountain Man, whose reputation had spread throughout the East.

He had not long to wait. Jim Bridger was as eager to talk to emigrants as they were to talk to him. As usual, Brigham's keen gray eyes studied the man carefully. They took in the gaunt figure, the bearded face, the slouchy clothing. So much was characteristic of the Mountain Men. But there was something that was not so common among these hardy, outdoor fellows—a shiftiness in the eyes. Brigham felt an instant distrust of the man, but he spoke courteously.

"Mr. Bridger, I understand that you are thoroughly acquainted with the West?"

"I sure am. Know it better'n any livin' soul, danged if I don't. 'Twas Jim Bridger that discovered the big lake of salt water. 'Twas Jim Bridger that stayed here an' built a fort when others went skedaddling to the cities. What is it ye'd like to know about the West?"

"Well, take a look at this map, Mr. Bridger. I'm wondering whether it is accurate. It shows a valley to the east of the Great Salt Lake—a valley rimmed by mountains. I was thinking—"

Jim Bridger stared at the map. Then he grunted in disgust. "I met that Captain Frémont's party when they wuz out here some years ago. I don't see how he could make a map of the country, when all he did wuz stay on the plain roads. Now me, I've been on every stream, crossed every mounting—"

"What do you think of the valley of the Great Salt Lake?"

"I love it! It's my Paradise. I tell ye, if anyone ever settles in that country, I'll settle there with 'em. There's jest one thing," he went on as he saw the delighted look on his listener's face, "ye couldn't raise no grain there. No, sir! The frosts would kill it in no time. And the water's so danged cold comin' out of the mountings, it would freeze the seeds an' keep 'em from growin' at all. No, sir! It wouldn't be wise to take a large number of people to the Great Salt Lake."

Brigham's pleased smile died. He shook his head thoughtfully. "I can't believe that, sir. It seems strange—"

"Wal, I kin tell ye it's the truth. I've lived here in the mountings most of my life—come out when I was a younker of seventeen—an' I know what I'm talkin' about. Even the Injuns are a miserable crew. They live on crickets an' ants

an' sech. An' there's no water exceptin' those icy cold mounting streams. Ye can't raise nothin' there."

Brigham asked patiently, "Have you tried to, sir?"

"Have I tried? Gar, there's no need to try anythin' so open-
an-shet as that. Why, I'll tell ye what, Mister Young. I'd
give a thousand dollars if I knowed thet an ear of corn
could be ripened in these mountings. I've been here twenty
years and tried it in vain, over an' over agin."

"Give me a little time," Brigham smiled grimly, "and I'll
show you what can be done!"

His counselors gathered around, worry on their faces.

"The report is always the same—"

"I don't give a fig for their reports!" Brigham said curtly.
"Perhaps the next man we meet will have a different story
to tell."

The next man they met was one of their own people. On
the last day of June, while the caravan was camped on the
Green River, three weary, dust-covered horsemen rode in.
Brigham, notified of their approach, was watching them,
but it was not until they were right in the camp that he
recognized who they were. He hurried forward.

"Brother Samuel! What brings you here? How are the
Saints in California? Nothing's happened, I hope—"

Sam Brannan tumbled wearily from his horse. "We've
been riding day and night to reach you before you turned
southward. Thank heavens we made it."

"So I see. But why have you come? Has anything happened?"

"The Saints are all right. We are in good health. Our
colony is flourishing—"

"Then why this express to meet us?"

"You know when I sailed from New York City last year
in the ship *Brooklyn,* it was planned that I'd take my company of two hundred and thirty-five Saints to California by
sea—around Cape Horn. Then I would bring them over-

land to whatever place you'd chosen for our gathering."

Brigham nodded impatiently.

"Well, as you know from the letters I sent back, we reached Yerba Buena all right. And we found a country such as we had never dreamed of. Oh, President Young, it is truly a Land of Promise!"

"California?" Brigham muttered angrily. "If it is so wonderful we would not be left in peace there as much as five years!"

"Oh, but we would! The climate is wonderful—mild and moist! Things grow luxuriantly all the year around. When we left in April, flowers were blooming; the trees were in blossom. The valleys stretch to the mountains as inviting as cultivated parks. The soil—oh, I haven't words to describe it!"

One of the listening men sighed, "In Upper California, Oh!" Brigham's stern look stopped him.

"We considered these things before we left Iowa," he said. "The Prophet said to go to the basin of the Great Salt Lake, to the tops of the mountains. I feel we should trust the Prophet."

"But we didn't know then what we'd find in California!" Brannan protested. "Oh, believe me, President Young, that desert around the Great Salt Lake is a terrible place. As we came through the mountains from California on this trip, we saw the bones of one party. They had been trapped by that desert; their animals had died; and they weren't able to get through the mountains before the winter blizzards set in."

Heber asked, "Was that the party led by George and Jacob Donner?"

Brannan nodded.

"I heard them speak about the party at Fort Laramie," Heber went on. "Someone was asking how they got through."

"Most of them didn't. And it was because of that desert,"

Brannan answered grimly. Then he turned to Brigham Young. "How can you plant twenty thousand people in such a place? They will all perish!" He was pleading, close to tears.

Orson Pratt spoke up. "There is strength in numbers. Each succeeding train will add to our strength."

"But why?" Brannan insisted. "We left Yerba Buena in April and have traveled day and night to save you from making the wrong decision. Why should you go down into that barren desert when a merciful land is waiting? . . . where you can raise food for a million souls without effort. Mountains at your back to protect you from invasion from the States; and the wide sea in front of you as a protection, or as a means of escape, should escape ever be necessary."

Brigham was stroking his chin thoughtfully, listening to the man's impassioned plea.

"Why, sir, there the Saints can prosper and grow strong. The world will look upon us with envy. We, who were driven out in poverty, will rise up in wealth. But the Salt Lake Valley—oh, sir, that is a place none will envy us. No one would take it as a gift!"

Brigham's hand stopped stroking his chin. His eyes lighted with determination.

"Brother Samuel, if there is a place on this earth that no one else wants, that is the place I am hunting for. Tomorrow we move on to the valley of the Great Salt Lake."

Now there were no more delays to inquire about the valley, or the road thither. The caravan turned southward toward the frightening barrier of the mountains. Traveling was difficult, the way often seeming impassable. But Brigham neither hesitated nor permitted hesitation.

When they came to steep slopes where the loaded wagons were in danger of rolling down upon the teams, the wheels were locked and heavy logs fastened to them to hold them back. When they came to sheer precipices, the wagons were roped and let down hand over hand. Trees were felled; bridges were built across streams and chasms. But the caravan moved on.

Sam Brannan and his two companions, though desperately disappointed at having failed in their mission, went on with the caravan. They would rest a few days at the journey's end and then go on back to California.

As Brigham's train moved into higher and higher altitudes, many fell sick with "mountain fever." They had reached the Bear River when Brigham himself became so ill that he could travel no farther. But he was impatient to reach his goal.

He called some of his leading men to his bedside.

"Brother Orson," he said to Orson Pratt, "select a small company and go on ahead. Find out the best road—and when you come out of the mountains into the valley, bear to the north. Begin to plow at once, in order to get potatoes in before it is too late in the season. I can't tell how long I'll be detained here—and we must not delay."

Orson looked at his beloved leader. Had he come this far only to be deprived of seeing the new Zion?

Brigham noticed the look in his companion's eyes. "Have faith, Brother Orson. And make haste."

"But how shall we plow, if the land is as dry and as hard as we have been told?" one of the men asked.

Brigham sighed impatiently. "There'll be a stream of some kind! Throw up a dam and turn the water onto the land to soak it. Then you can use your plows."

Orson Pratt set out with a company of twenty-three wagons, and the next day Brigham ordered the main body of the caravan to go forward. He himself was still too ill to move. His friend Heber, anxious over his leader's condition, called a prayer meeting to petition that Brigham's health would be restored.

The next day Brigham felt better. Wilford Woodruff had

his own comfortable light wagon fitted up with a bed, and Brigham was transferred to this vehicle. So, in three separate divisions, the impatient Saints moved over the mountains and down the canyons toward a goal none of them had yet seen.

The main company came out of the mountains into the wide, beautiful valley, rimmed on three sides by snow-capped mountains and on the west by the silvery lake. They bore to the north, as Brigham had advised, and found a stream there, crystal clear and cold. Even before camp was made the plows were unpacked from the wagons and teams harnessed to them. But the plows could not cut into the hard-baked desert soil.

Orson Pratt recalled what Brigham had said in impatience. He passed the word along. Immediately, a dam was put across the mountain stream and the water was turned out of its channel onto the hard and thirsty ground.

On the afternoon of July 23rd, Brigham Young, lying on the improvised bed in Wilford Woodruff's carriage, caught his first glimpse of the valley. It was only a glimpse, however, seen between the timbered shoulders of two hills. Brigham raised up on his elbow and stared. Then he sank back and closed his eyes. Before his closed lids rose a picture of the city to be—a city such as his beloved Joseph would have planned.

They camped that night in the canyon and the next morning Wilford Woodruff drove his carriage out of the mountains. The whole wide valley lay before them. Woodruff turned his carriage halfway around, open to the west, so the sick man could look out at the amazing sight—the wide, gently sloping valley, bordered by mountain and lake, traversed by willow-edged streams.

Brigham Young let his eyes drink in the whole lovely scene. Then he sighed contentedly.

"It is enough," he said. "This is the right place. Drive on."

CHAPTER FIFTEEN

A SHOW OF HANDS

>>>->>>->>>->>>->>>->>>->>>->>>->>>->>>

When Wilford Woodruff drove his light wagon up to the camp that Saturday afternoon, the men dropped their hoes and plows and came running to greet their leader.

"How's President Young?" "How's Brother Brigham?" they asked anxiously. Brigham raised himself on his elbow and greeted them happily.

"You have selected the best place for the camp," he said approvingly, looking out at the two forks of the canyon stream between which the wagons were drawn up. Then that familiar smile quirked his lips. "And I see you have begun to plow."

"Yes," Orson Pratt said. "The ground was even harder than I had imagined, so I put in a dam, as you suggested. And the brethren have got some of their seed potatoes planted."

Wilford Woodruff shook the lines impatiently. "I've a bushel of seed potatoes to plant," he observed. "Which is Brother Brigham's tent? I'll just deposit him and get to my planting."

"It's past midday and you have not stopped for lunch," Orson remarked. "Better wait until after you eat."

"I don't care about eating. I'm going to get those potatoes into the ground before I stop to do anything else!"

Brigham himself was still too weak to plow or plant. But he was pleased at the energy of his counselors.

As the men worked, a band of fifteen Indians came to watch them "throw the dirt," as the natives called plowing. They had never before seen anything like this and were curious, wondering what sort of "medicine" the white man was using. The little band was led by Wanship, a Ute chieftain, and his son Jim. The pioneers had had to pass through Wanship's territory, and he had kept his eyes upon them.

"Give them presents," Brigham advised. "Try to keep friendly with them, but do not let them become too familiar. We must do nothing to provoke them if we can help it." His keen gray eyes roamed over the valley. "Here we are— a handful of white people, with the nearest succor a thousand miles away in any direction. I don't know how many warriors that chieftain can call upon, but certainly more men than we have. It will be far cheaper to feed them than to fight them!"

The next day was Sunday and, true to their principles, the pioneers did no work on that day. Instead, they held regular religious services.

Brigham, too weak to stand, addressed his people as he sat in an armchair placed upon an overturned wagon bed. He was pale and trembling, but his voice was firm and strong.

"We have found the place, Brethren. I feel to give praise that we have come through without the loss of a single human life. What animals we have lost have been lost through our own carelessness or rashness. I feel that the Prophet Joseph is rejoicing with us today. We have traveled a thousand miles from Winter Quarters and have arrived safely here in the tops of the mountains.

"Now, I want to tell you some of the rules we must obey in this place. There will be no working or hunting on the Sabbath day. There will be no buying or selling of land. This valley has been given to us all equally and each man's inheritance will be measured out to him according to his needs. He may plant it to anything he wishes, but if he does not cultivate it, we will take it from him and give it to those who will make it produce."

His listeners looked at each other and nodded. That was right. If a man did not raise food for himself and his family, someone else would have to care for them. And each man was going to have enough to do without being burdened by the shiftless and the lazy.

"There will be no private ownership of water or of timber," Brigham went on. "Water, here, is as necessary to life as is air, and no man can have the right to charge his neighbor for it."

At the evening services Orson Pratt spoke. He chose for his text "How beautiful upon the mountains are the feet of him that bringeth good tidings, that publisheth peace." As he spoke, his listeners lifted their eyes to the rosy hills that rimmed them in, and when he finished their voices broke spontaneously into song.

> "The morning breaks, the shadows flee;
> Lo! Zion's standard is unfurled!
> The dawning of a brighter day
> Majestic rises on the world."

On Monday, Brigham could not bear to stay in bed any longer. Weak as he was, he mounted a horse and rode with some of his friends to the summit of a peak north of their camp. Here, high above their companions, they stuck the standard of a pennant into the ground, and the mountain breeze caught and unfurled it against the sky—Zion's ensign.

Wilford Woodruff shouted in joy, "Let us name this Ensign Peak!"

From their vantage point they could look out over the whole valley. To the east were the snow-capped Wasatch Mountains, curving southward in a sheltering arm almost half way around the valley. At the southernmost tip of the valley was a narrow, almost imperceptible passageway between the Wasatch Mountains and the range that skirted the valley on the west, up to the silver waters of the lake. Those glittering waters were broken here and there by the rocky surface of barren islands.

"It is the most beautiful sight my eyes have ever beheld!" sighed Brigham. "I am content. Here in this solitude we should be able to hear the voice of God."

"Some of the brethren are eager to go out exploring. Some think they can find better places—more abundant water, closer timber, richer earth—" Heber began, but Brigham shook his head.

"They are at liberty to explore, but I am confident they will return here and say this is the best place of all."

Brigham himself, however, wanted to know more about the immediate vicinity of his new home. With companions he rode northward and investigated some hot springs they found there. He decided that they had definite health-giving properties. He rode westward around the southern tip of the lake and bathed in the salty waters. He studied the willow-bordered stream that emptied into the lake.

"We should call this stream the western Jordan," he exclaimed. "It empties into a dead sea just as the biblical River Jordan does."

Brigham did not use up many days in exploration. He knew that he must return to Winter Quarters before winter set in. So he told his people decidedly, "Now we must get to work and build a stockade so those who remain here through the winter will be safe from the Indians."

Walking to a spot between the two forks of the stream, he struck his cane into the ground, saying, "Here we will build a temple to our God."

Wilford Woodruff marked the place with a stake.

"We will lay our city out around that temple," Brigham

went on with enthusiasm. "It will be a city as beautiful as Nauvoo, the City of Joseph."

Then he went on to outline the details of his city plan: There would be blocks of ten acres each, laid out foursquare, with all streets running due north and south, due east and west. Each block would be divided into eight equal lots. Each house should be placed in the center of its lot, parallel to its neighbors, and all at the same distance from the street.

"Streets and sidewalks will be uniformly wide, with trees planted along them. And between the streets and sidewalks we'll have ditches into which we'll run these clear mountain streams. We'll permit no filth to stand in yards or streets, and we'll keep everything clean and orderly."

On Thursday of that first week Brigham and his counselors went out to meet the Mormon Battalion boys and the rest of the Mississippi Saints, who were coming in from Pueblo, where they had spent the winter.

There was a goodly company of tanned young men, some riding horseback, some in wagons, some walking. Heber's black eyes twinkled when he saw them.

"Aren't they a sight to behold, Brother Brigham? Dressed in buckskin, all spangled up with porcupine quills, with long hair and beards—they look like real Mountain Men."

The men were singing as they marched out of Emigration Canyon.

> "A band of Mormons here we are
> And may kind Heaven's watchful care
> Preserve us from the Devil's fleet
> Till we again our friends shall meet
> And see fine times!"

One of the buckskin-clad men drew rein and held out his hand. "Hello, there, President Young!"

Brigham grasped the hand and squinted to get a look at the face behind the heavy beard.

"John Steele!" he exclaimed. "How are you? And how's Sister Steele? She went along with the battalion, if I recollect rightly, to cook for you men."

"She's in a wagon back there. We've been hurrying the band along so that our first child might be born in the valley."

"Have you suffered much?"

Steele shrugged. "Some, of course. But it was worth it. We started out on foot and in rags and we come back riding and dressed in buckskin. We left with nothing and we have brought back guns and ammunition—and something that may be better still."

"What's that?" Brigham asked.

"My knapsack's plumb full of good white Taos wheat!"

"Good! Good! I hope the others have been as thoughtful."

"They have. We all brought all the seeds or grain we could get hold of."

Men singing, the "Battalion Boys" marched bravely down the hillside and into the city. With these fresh, energetic young fellows in camp, the work progressed rapidly. A road was laid to the canyon to bring out timber; men were appointed to take care of that job. Others were named to direct the making of sun-dried bricks, or adobies, from the clayey soil. Still others were appointed as builders, hunters, blacksmiths, herders. A bowery was erected for meetings.

Brigham took off his coat, rolled up his sleeves and worked with the others. He knew that other members of his family would be coming along with Parley Pratt and John Taylor, and a house of some sort must be ready for them.

To save time, labor and material, Brigham ordered the stockade built first of all. Its wall could then be used as the outer wall of the cabins. These faced the center of a hollow square and were set end to end in a continuous row. Thus each man had to build only the front and one end of his own cabin, as the stockade and his next neighbor provided the other two walls of the one-room structure. The work went along at an amazing rate.

On August 9th, less than two weeks after the arrival of the Mormon Battalion boys, Brigham was called to John Steele's tent.

"President Young," Steele said proudly, "my wife has just given birth to a fine baby girl. I'd like to name her for you, sir."

Brigham's eyes twinkled. "How'll she like being called Briggy?"

"Well, I sort of had it figured out, we'd name her Young and then give her a girl's name, too. Young Elizabeth Steele we thought would be a good name. What do you say, sir?"

Brigham agreed seriously, "I feel that you honor me, Brother John. Naming the first white child born in the valley for me."

"It's little enough that we can do for you, President Young. You've done so much for all of us—been like a father to us at Winter Quarters, and here, too. If it'd been a boy, I'd sure like to have named him Brigham."

Brigham was touched. He remembered all the little Josephs born at Kirtland and Nauvoo, and he wondered if he had truly managed to win such a place of affection in his followers' hearts.

On Sunday, August 22nd, just one month after the first party had entered the valley, Brigham was ready to return to Winter Quarters to oversee the bringing out of the rest of the Saints. He called his people together to instruct them what to do while he was gone. But first he reviewed the achievements of the past four weeks.

"The fort is so nearly finished that the first families can move into their houses at once. Twenty-nine cabins are finished. Fifty-three acres are plowed and planted to buckwheat, corn, potatoes and gardens. Keep those acres fenced and protected from cattle. I would rather see ten acres planted and fenced than fifty planted for the sake of roving cattle."

He paused to let his words sink into his hearers' minds and then went on, "Complete the fort before you do anything else. Stay right here until I return next summer. Brother John Taylor will be in charge, but I want every one of you to be in charge of himself and his family!"

His blue eyes moved over the crowd, judging them. Perhaps his words sounded a good deal like a father leaving his family and telling them how to manage while he was gone. But that's how it was, Brigham thought wryly. He felt like a father and they were much like children—waiting to be advised and instructed in these strange surroundings.

He mounted his waiting horse and then, standing up in the stirrups, he waved his hand at the solemn group watching him off. "God keep all who tarry!" he cried cheerfully. "I feel well." He slapped the reins against the horse's neck and rode off to join his companions who had left the day before and were waiting for him at a camp on the Bear River.

The return to Winter Quarters was an even more trying journey than the outward trip had been. The road was filled, it seemed, with caravans of people hastening to get across the mountains before winter set in. Among these, the returning Saints found Parley P. Pratt's company, which had set out without proper provision and was in dire straits when they were met. The next day they came upon John Taylor's company, the last of the emigrating Saints for this season.

In these groups were the old and sick, women and children, widows who had no one to do the strenuous work of driving the wagons up and down the steep mountainsides and had to rely on others. The vast throngs of emigrant trains going to Oregon had used up the game and the forage, and the late-comers had found progress slow and difficult.

The returning pioneers, going back over a route laid bare by these oncoming thousands, were themselves in difficulties. By the time they reached the Sioux country, Indians had stolen many of their horses, and the men who had been riding had to give up their saddle horses to pull wagons.

Brigham, smiling wryly, stepped out of the saddle and said, "I am inviting all the brethren to take a walk with me to Winter Quarters!"

In spite of lack of food and forage, Indian annoyances and other trials, the party came at last within sight of their goal. Here Brigham stopped the caravan and addressed his companions. He thanked them for their loyalty and co-operation and asked them to join in a prayer of thanksgiving that they had made the entire trip to the Great Salt Lake and back without loss of a man.

They drove into Winter Quarters late that afternoon. The streets were crowded with men and women and children, shouting "Hosanna!" Joyful greetings mingled with tears and questions. There was a great distribution of letters from those left behind in the valley.

As the people crowded around Brigham, trying to shake his hand, touch his coat, ask him a question, his blue eyes searched for and found his own children and their mothers. They, too, wanted to touch their father, to welcome him back, and finally the eager neighbors drew back and let young Joseph and Brigham and the other children reach their father and receive his greeting. He gathered them to him, old and young, embracing them, laughingly. But he reserved his tender greeting of the mothers for the seclusion of their cabins.

At Mary Ann's little cabin that night, Brigham sank wearily into a chair. "It's been a long, hard journey," he sighed. "I've been sick and discouraged at times. Sometimes I've felt as if the pleasantest thing I could do would be just to lie down and wait for Judgment Day."

Mary Ann smiled sadly. "I know. But I've a mind you didn't tell your thoughts to the others."

The weariness left Brigham's blue eyes and a tenderness softened them. "No, it would have been a mighty poor thing to do."

There was much to be done that winter. The Saints had to be moved from the land of the Omahas back to the eastern side of the river, thus abandoning Winter Quarters for the inadequate little settlements on that side of the river. The Saints had got along well with the Indians; they had helped these Lamanites as Brigham had promised. And the Indians had given the Mormons little trouble. But the Indian agents in charge of this area did not approve of such friendly dealings between the white men and the "savages." They insisted that the Saints move off of the Omahas' lands.

Brigham took time to make a personal visit to the Omaha chieftain to thank him for his help and friendship and to assure him that the Saints appreciated what the Omahas had done for them. Then he carefully explained that the majority of the Saints would leave for the West early the next spring. Those who remained would settle on the eastern bank of the river, in the land of the Potawatomis; but their friendship for their Omaha brothers would not be diminished.

Another problem Brigham had to tackle was that of the many converts who were clamoring to be brought to Zion. And more missionaries must be sent out to all lands, to win more converts, who would just add to the problem. But most important of all, the organization of the church had to be revised.

Under Joseph Smith the church had been governed by a president with two counselors. The quorum of Twelve Apostles had been set aside to do missionary work. Since Joseph's death, however, the apostles had had to stay home much of the time to act as the presidency of the church.

They had been kept so busy taking care of the harassed Saints that the missionary work had had to be handed over to others. Now Brigham felt it was time to reinstate the old organization.

He called the apostles to a meeting at Orson Hyde's house in Kanesville, a settlement near Winter Quarters that had been named for Colonel Kane. At that meeting, Orson Hyde proposed that Brigham Young be made president of the church and that he choose two counselors, and that three others be named to the Quorum of Twelve to perfect the organization. The suggestion was unanimously approved.

Brigham lost no time in naming his counselors. His long-time friend Heber Kimball was chosen first counselor and Dr. Willard Richards second. Later their places in the Twelve were filled from the ranks of the loyal members.

According to Mormon practice, none of these appointments was effective until ratified by the church membership at large. Brigham called a conference, and so many came that the usual meetinghouse could not hold them all.

"We'll have to have a tabernacle," Brigham said. "The conference will be postponed until we can build one."

In less than a week the energetic members had built a log tabernacle that could hold a thousand people. It was filled to overflowing when, on December 27th, 1847, Brigham Young asked his people if they wanted him as president of the Church of Jesus Christ of Latter-day Saints.

"If you do," he finished, "please indicate it by a show of hands!"

The hall blossomed with hands raised in enthusiastic approval.

"Contrary by the same sign!"

Not a hand was raised.

Brigham turned to Heber. Tears glistened in his eyes. "This is one of the happiest days of my life!" he said reverently.

CHAPTER SIXTEEN

MIRACLE IN THE DESERT

->>>->>>->>>->>>->>>->>>->>>->>>->>>->>>

On a beautiful morning toward the end of May, 1848, Brigham Young once more turned his back to the East, never again to return. He had waited until the last wagon had pulled out. Winter Quarters with its eight hundred log houses, its brush huts and dugouts, its log tabernacle and its gardens, was practically abandoned. Only a few Saints remained to take care of the fields and keep things in readiness to serve the emigrants who would be coming in from foreign missions. And they had been moved from Winter Quarters itself onto Potawatomi lands across the river.

Brigham, leaving his own sturdy log house, said grimly to Heber, "This is the fifth time I have left my home and property since I embraced the gospel!"

Heber smiled wryly, "I know. I've been right with you— Mendon, Kirtland, Far West, Nauvoo and now Winter Quarters!"

"We must build up a kingdom so strong and powerful that no one can drive us out of it. I had thought we were going to have plenty of time for this, out there by ourselves in the mountains. But these stories of gold in California—they are disquieting!"

Heber's black eyes twinkled. "And to think our Mormon Battalion boys were right there, on the spot—Henry Bigler was one of them. Maybe those battalion boys shouldn't have

147

been left to work in California. Then our people might not have heard of the gold quite so soon."

"Well, we needed the money they could earn. But now Brother John Taylor writes that some of the Saints are itching to leave the valley to go running off to the gold fields. We'll have to get out there and put an end to that nonsense!" said Brigham, who well understood that he had a far different problem this summer than he had faced the year before. That first company had been made up of carefully chosen men. It was small, and all but five were capable and strong.

This time he had three hundred and ninety-seven wagons carrying more than one thousand two hundred people. Among these were widows and children, the sick and aged, many who would have to be cared for by others. The wagons were heavily loaded because the people did not want to leave all their precious things behind. Organs, cupboards and other massive pieces weighted down the wagons and made progress slow.

Moreover, these hundreds of people were not all of one mind. There were arguments and quarrels among them. Some became discouraged and turned back. Provisions ran low and sickness and accidents caused great suffering. Many died and were buried beside the trail. Altogether, it was a rather desperate caravan that wound across the prairies that summer, and only the indomitable courage and perseverance of their leader kept them toiling onward.

Brigham relied on music to help him. Often as the weary, dusty, wavering line moved along, he would start singing one of the courageous songs his people knew. It might be

> To the West, to the West!
> To the land of the free!

Or, more likely if Brigham started the song it would be a hymn:

"Angels from heaven and truth from earth
Have met and both have record borne;
Thus Zion's light is bursting forth,
To bring her ransomed children home."

For the most part, Brigham was well pleased with his followers. But at times disagreements arose; delays caused resentment; worry made tempers short. Then the people would begin to bicker among themselves, or grumble about their hardships. And Brigham would lose patience.

He was gentle and helpful to those really in trouble. When a child died on the journey, the parents came to Brigham for comfort. When a parent died, the children sought the sheltering arms of Mother Young. But grumblers, Brigham could not endure.

One day when they had reached the Sweetwater and the discontented mutterings had reached a new volume, he at last gave vent to his contempt for the bickering. He went over to his carriage, hitched up his own team and climbed onto the seat. He cast a glance out at the people who stood watching him, wondering what he meant to do.

"I am going to the valley!" he announced curtly. "If anybody wants to follow, the road is open!"

He put the whip to the horses and drove away, not looking back.

For eighteen miles he rode alone. Then he pulled up in the shade of some trees and waited. Before long his lips quirked with amusement and his impatience vanished. Over the nearest hill appeared a wagon. As it began to descend the slope, another came into sight, then another. The teams were stepping briskly along, the drivers obviously in a hurry to catch up with their leader.

On September 20th, Brigham drove out of the canyon and looked again upon his valley. His heart lifted. Where fourteen months before had been only sagebrush and sand,

with no sign of human habitation, now he saw a thriving
village. Nearly five hundred buildings lay before him, standing in the neat, orderly rows he had planned for his city.
In the silence of the autumn afternoon he could hear the
hum of saw and flour mills erected on the canyon streams.
He could see the twelve miles of fencing around more than
five thousand acres of cultivated land. The fields were
golden with ripening grain.

Exultantly Brigham turned to Heber and quoted from
Isaiah, "The wilderness and the solitary place shall be glad
for them and the desert shall rejoice and blossom as the
rose!"

The Saints came out to welcome their leader, singing
hymns and chanting hosannas. He rode through the streets
like a conquering hero—this sturdy, New England-born farm
boy, whose powerful leadership was responsible for transporting thousands from the lush meadows of the East into
this barren, sandy valley.

Brigham didn't take time to savor his triumph, nor to rest
after those arduous one hundred and sixteen days on the
trail. As soon as he stepped out of his carriage, the people
flocked around him with their complaints and troubles. He
immediately called a meeting of his elders to learn what had
taken place here in his absence. And there he heard of the
miracle of the sea gulls.

Elder John Taylor related the event: "It was late in May
that it happened. We had worked hard to get as many acres
planted as possible. We'd gone hungry ourselves in order
to have wheat and corn for planting. Since the winter was
mild, we had been able to sow some two thousand acres to
fall wheat.

"It sprouted early and we watched with grateful hearts
the young shoots appear and grow. It looked as if we should
have a bountiful harvest.

"But just as the fields were gloriously green, the crickets came!"

Brigham frowned with disgust. He remembered the crickets—loathsome black insects that the miserable Indians of the valley had been catching and eating when the pioneers first came.

Elder Taylor sighed. "We thought at first it was a storm cloud lowering on the hills. Then we decided it must be smoke from brush fires started by the Indians. But before long we discovered that it was worse than either of these. Millions of these black crickets came hopping down the hillsides and onto our fields. They lighted on the young wheat, climbed up the stalks, stripping off every leaf, every budding head, as they went. They threatened to take our entire crop. We saw starvation facing us."

"Was there no way to fight them?"

"We fought them! Every man, woman and child was out fighting all day long. We tried everything—fire just drove them onto new fields. In small fields, boys would beat the stalks, carrying a rope taut between them, walking back and forth, whipping the insects from the wheat. But that didn't stop them. As soon as the boys had passed the crickets leaped up and began their work again.

"We dug trenches and drove millions into these and burned or drowned them. But it didn't seem to lessen the fearful hordes at all. We prayed—" he hesitated, remembering the weary men and women, boys and girls, kneeling in the fields, their heads bowed, their hands upraised in supplication.

"And then?" Brigham asked.

"And then a white cloud seemed to rise from the lake. We were horrified to see the gulls coming. We thought it was another disaster. But we were wrong. It was not a disaster. Our prayers had been answered.

"The gulls lighted on the fields and began to devour the

crickets. We watched in amazement, but with little hope. The gulls could not eat all those crickets. When they had eaten all they wished, they would fly away and leave us to the mercy of the insects.

"But we'd reckoned without the Lord. When the gulls had eaten all they could hold, they disgorged the dead insects and started to eat again. Our crops were saved.

"I declared that we should give thanks by a three-day fast and prayer, and the Saints joined in with fervent hearts. It was a blessing upon us that we shall never forget!"

Brigham nodded thoughtfully. "The Saints did their part and the Lord did His. I've always known that He will help us, if we will work and pray!"

That winter the people in the valley were very poor. Men and women went dressed in burlap or bed ticking and felt lucky to have a wolfskin or deerskin to help keep out the cold. And of course some began to grumble.

Heber Kimball rose up in meeting one Sunday and reproved them roundly for their lack of hopefulness.

"You complain of poverty, of scarcity of food and clothing, of high prices. Let me tell you that within three years you will buy states' goods in the streets of this city more cheaply than you can purchase them in St. Louis or New York!"

He sat down, wiping his face with his handkerchief. One of the elders leaned toward him.

"I can't believe that, Brother Heber!" he said.

Heber sighed. "I guess the Spirit left me and the man spoke. I am afraid I missed it this time!"

But he hadn't missed it. During the coming summer the forty-niners, rushing to the gold fields, brought a measure of prosperity to the Saints. Their city—the City of the Great Salt Lake, as they called it—was just about halfway between the States on the east and California on the west. It became the great national way station or resting place. Here, heavily laden wagons were stripped of all but essentials before the threat of the desert and the high Sierras. Furniture, clothing and provisions could be purchased for almost anything. And here, too, jaded teams were traded for the fat horses and oxen and mules of the Saints. Heber's prediction had come true, and the Saints had been able to procure many of the necessities and some of the luxuries they themselves had left behind them.

Some of the people in the valley caught the "gold fever" and itched to get away and find their fortunes. Brigham Young was annoyed at their "foolishness." He was convinced that only through poverty and work could the Saints build up a strong Zion. Riches would make them weak.

"I tell you, you will do better right here than you will by going to the gold mines. I can stand in my door and see where there are untold millions of the rich treasures of the earth—gold and silver. But the time has not come for the Saints to dig gold. It is our duty to develop the agricultural resources of the country!"

Though he was irritated by those who wanted to leave the valley to seek gold, he was pleased with the ones who had gone east and west and north and south in the Great Basin to establish settlements in the rich valleys of the mountains.

During that very first winter, David and Perregrine Sessions had gone ten miles north of the fort to build homes for their families in a lush meadow. They called the place Sessions' Settlement. Others had gone still farther north, as far as Bear River. Fort Buenaventura at Ogden's Hole had been purchased from Miles Goodyear, and a settlement was started there. Parley P. Pratt had led a group southward to the site of the old fort of Etienne Provot on Utah Lake and had decided that it would be an excellent location for another settlement.

Other groups had gone east into the lush, Alpine-like

canyons of the Wasatch, while still others went westward
to the valleys south of the lake. So that, by the time Brigham
returned from Winter Quarters a good deal of exploration
of the Great Basin had been completed and a number of
settlements started.

By the spring of 1849 Brigham's idea of the Mormon
Empire was firmly set and the pattern was clear. In March
he sent a petition to President Zachary Taylor, asking him
to establish territorial government in the "State of Deseret."
The name of the new territory, taken from the Book of
Mormon, meant the honey bee. The symbol of the territory
would be the beehive, and its motto, "Industry."

The "State of Deseret," as Brigham saw it, included a vast
amount of land—the entire Great Basin. It would be bounded
on the north by Oregon, on the south by Mexico, on the east
by the Rockies and on the west by the Sierra Nevadas.

While the Saints waited for action in Washington, they
set up their own provisional government. Naturally, Brigham
Young was named governor, and the other offices were distributed among the church leaders.

By July 24th, exactly two years after their first entrance
into the valley, the Mormons had built a city, established
colonies up and down and across the Great Basin and set
up a government.

"It is time to celebrate," Brigham announced. "The anniversary of our entrance into Zion shall be set aside as a
day of rejoicing and thanksgiving."

The harvest was plentiful, the people well clothed and
their homes fairly comfortable. They felt happy and prosperous and confident. Tables were spread in the bowery
and more than a thousand sat down to enjoy the feast. Brigham gave the address of the day. He recounted the trials
and tribulations the people had suffered, their expulsion
from New York, Ohio, Missouri and Illinois, their long trek
across the plains and mountains.

"We came to these mountains because we had no place else to go," he said. "But we have surmounted our difficulties and can assemble in peace here in the chambers of the mountains. And if they'll just leave us alone here for ten years, we'll never have to ask odds of anyone again!"

CHAPTER SEVENTEEN

IT'S CHEAPER TO FEED THEM

->>>->>>->>>->>>->>>->>>->>>->>>->>>->>>

The Book of Mormon relates that the Indians of the American continent are descended from the ancient Israelites. Their ancestors had escaped from Jerusalem and made their way to this continent. Their dark skins had been given them as a punishment when they strayed from the paths of righteousness. The Mormons believed it was their duty to teach these unfortunate people the gospel and to lift them out of their savage ways into the life they rightfully should have.

From the very first days of the church, missionaries had gone out among the Indian tribes to preach to them and to baptize them into the faith. One of the favorite hymns sung at Nauvoo was addressed to the Indians, or Lamanites, as the Saints called them, since they were supposed to be the direct descendants of an early prophet named Laman.

"Oh, stop and tell me, Red Man,
   Who are you, why you roam,
   And how you get your living;
   Have you no God, no home?

"Before your nation knew us,
   Some thousand moons ago,
   Our father fell in darkness
   And wandered to and fro.

156

"Yet hope within us lingers,
As if the Spirit spoke,
He'll come for your redemption
And break your Gentile yoke."

Wherever the Saints had found themselves among Indians, they had treated the natives with courtesy and consideration. This had repaid them well. Although on their journey to the Great Basin, the Mormons had lost some horses and cattle, they had not been badly troubled, and they had little reason to feel a great fear of the savages.

But out in the mountains, a thousand miles from any help, the Saints looked warily at the natives. Brigham himself had no doubt how the Indians should be handled. He told his people:

"Do not encourage them to come into your camps. But if they come, give them presents of food and clothing. Never steal from an Indian and never wrong one in any way." By way of emphasis he added, "It is cheaper to feed them than to fight them."

As Mormon settlements spread out over the floor of the Great Basin, the Saints did not follow their leader's advice. They became friendly with the natives, invited them into the cabins, let the boys race with the Indian youths and in many ways were lax in maintaining the attitude suggested by Brigham. And then there was trouble, and the settlers came hurrying to Brigham with complaints and with pleas for help. Then the leader would say again:

"Stockade your fort and attend to your own affairs and let the Indians take care of theirs. Let your women and children stay in the fort and the Indians out. If you mix with them promiscuously, you must continue to receive such treatment from them as they please to give."

As a rule the Indians were friendly and welcomed the Mormons to their grounds. Some of the chieftains even begged Brigham to send his people to teach their tribesmen how to farm. These natives saw at once that the Mormons were different from the other white men who had taken the red men's land. They called the Saints "Mormonee" to distinguish them from the "Mericats." They said, "Mormonee weino, Mormonee tick-a-boo (Friends). Make-em water ditch. Plant-em grain. Feed-em Indians."

Among the friendly chiefs were Wanship and Tabby to the northeast of the growing city, Washakie far to the north, Sowiette in the valley by Utah Lake, Kanosh and Sanpitch in the central part of the territory and old Chief Toquer at the southern end.

These chieftains performed many services for the newcomers. Washakie, a Shoshone chief, often camped near Pacific Springs on the Mormon road to the valley. He was helpful to the emigrant trains, aided them in finding lost cattle and horses, sometimes even provided native medicines for the ailing children.

Kanosh, a Pahvant chieftain, was known as the Peacemaker, because of his untiring efforts to settle difficulties between the two races. Wanship, a Snake, was an enemy of the Utes, but friendly to the Mormons who had settled on the neutral land between the two hostile nations.

Sowiette, king of the Utes, roamed the land south of this neutral ground. Before the first wagon train of pioneers came into the valley, this old chieftain was aware of what was happening. He called a council to decide what was to be done about the invasion of the whites. The wise old chieftain advised peace and co-operation. Some of his young braves disagreed with this policy. But later, when trouble arose, Sowiette could always be relied upon to protect the white man. At one time when the Utes had determined to attack Fort Utah, Sowiette warned the settlers and offered to lend some of his warriors to help defend them.

Down in the southern end of the territory, old Chief

Toquer wept when he learned that the Mormons were leaving the Indian mission. He said, "Now we will have no one to tell us about Shinob!" (God).

But there was one young Ute brave, a half brother of old Sowiette's, who caused Brigham plenty of trouble. This was Walkara, or Walker, the Hawk of the Mountains.

At Sowiette's council concerning the coming of the Mormons, Walkara had voted for war against the invaders. He was a dashing brave, over six feet tall, hawk nosed, keen eyed, with a band of two hundred young daredevils to do his bidding. They made their living by raiding California ranches to steal horses; by kidnaping Piede and Paiute children to sell as slaves to the Mexicans and Navahos; and by exacting tribute from the caravans that passed over the Spanish Trail on their journeys between the Pueblo de los Angeles and old Taos. These dashing raiders dressed richly, adorning themselves with much Navaho silver and turquoise, Mexican lace and velvet. And they took orders from no one but Walkara, their master.

This haughty chieftain was an unpredictable fellow. He deeply resented the coming of the Mormons. He was often insulted by their treatment of him. They were generous and courteous, it is true, but they did not observe Ute protocol. When Walkara was invited to eat at a white man's table, which happened often enough, his host was so stupid that he permitted his white squaw to sit at the same table. And there were other annoyances that irked the warlike chieftain.

There were larger resentments, also. The Mormons had not held a council with the Utes to ask permission to settle on this land. However, since the chief city was on neutral ground between the Snakes and the Utes, Walkara did not dare object too strenuously.

When, however, the Mormons went southward to Utah Lake, they entered Walkara's own traditional lands. Then he did object, but Brigham was able to win the haughty chief over. "You may have the lands," Walkara conceded, shrugging. "I don't care about that. But the streams are mine!" Yet the Mormons invariably made their settlements upon the banks of a stream, and Walkara hated this.

Late in 1850, President Millard Fillmore created the territory of Utah, and Brigham was named governor and superintendent of Indian Affairs. As governor, Brigham Young immediately issued an edict forbidding the slave traffic with Indian women and children. This struck at the very heart of the Utes' way of life. It seemed to them to be a highhanded and despotic move.

Against all these annoyances was balanced the Mormon consideration of the red man, the generous handing out of food and clothing, the planting of wide fields of grain, from which the lazy natives benefited. And there was the teaching about God, and that the red man was in very truth the brother and could be the equal of the whites.

Walkara was intrigued by this last idea. After many councils and some instruction in the principles of the Mormon religion, the haughty chief was baptized into the church. He expected that then and there he would be awarded every good thing the white man enjoyed, including a white squaw. This last was the dearest wish of the Ute's heart. He badgered Brigham time and again to concede this favor. Brigham replied very courteously that white women were not given away, but must choose their own husbands. Though he spoke with utmost seriousness, his blue eyes twinkled, and the twinkle did not escape the keen eyes of the Hawk of the Mountains.

For some six years the delicate balance between Walkara's resentments and his friendliness maintained a precarious equilibrium. But in July of 1853 an incident took place that disastrously upset the situation.

Walkara and his band were camped on Spring Creek, east of Utah Lake. Half a mile north of the Indian camp was the cabin of James Ivie. Some Utes came to Ivie's cabin to trade trout for flour. The squaw was content with the bargain she struck with Mrs. Ivie, but the brave with her was angered. He began to beat the squaw, telling her she had been cheated.

Ivie, coming up just then, interfered to protect the squaw. In the skirmish the brave was killed. This was excuse enough for Walkara to throw off all his friendly feelings toward the Mormons and give vent to the bitter hatred that lay deep in his heart. The Walker War was on.

All the rest of that summer and fall the Mormons knew the fear of Indian attack. Walkara was too wary to pit his forces against the stockades the settlers had built with their guns and cannons to repel any attack. But no man was safe if he left the fort to go out to the fields or canyons or along the roads from settlement to settlement.

Walkara and his men seemed to be everywhere. From Bear River in the north to the Rio Virgin in the south, reports kept coming in to Brigham. This traveler, or that small group of hunters, this isolated family or that trio out for wood, had been murdered by the Indians.

Brigham's attitude toward his erstwhile friend was a classic illustration of the Mormon leader's belief. He was profoundly sincere and genuine in his consideration of the natives. Other white settlers throughout the country had responded with gun and cannon, with retaliatory massacres, to any Indian attack. Brigham did not even use harsh words against his "enemy." Instead he scolded his own people for the state of affairs they had brought upon themselves.

"I have been trying for years," he told them angrily, "to get you people to establish yourselves in forts. With what success you can see. What of that? Nothing! Only I had no influence with the Saints to make them build forts. Now Brother Walker has taken the subject in hand, and his in-

fluence bids fair to be greater than Brother Young's. I think
he will compel the people to go into forts!"

When someone asked him if he did not intend to punish
Walkara, he answered, "It has taken us twenty-four years
to get where we are in the gospel. What can you expect of
these people who have had only six years to learn how to
behave?"

The Mormons had troops that could have been sent out
against the Utes, but Brigham ordered, "I want it distinctly
understood that no retaliation be made and no offense offered. I want all to act entirely on the defensive until fur-
ther orders."

At a meeting in the tabernacle, when the grumbling was
loud, Brigham emphasized his position. "How often I have
been asked what I intend to do with Walker. I say let him
alone severely. I have not made war on the Indians, nor
am I calculating to do it. My policy is to give them presents
and be kind to them. Instead of being Walker's enemy I
have sent him a great pile of tobacco to smoke when he is
lonely in the mountains. He is now at war with the only
friends he has upon this earth, and I want him to have
some tobacco to smoke."

With the tobacco, Brigham sent this characteristic letter
to the embittered Ute:

Great Salt Lake City, July 25, 1853

Captain Walker:

I send you some tobacco to smoke in the mountains
when you get lonesome. You are a fool for fighting your
best friends, for we are the best friends and the only
friends you have in the whole world. Everybody else
would kill you if they could get the chance. If you get
hungry, send some friendly Indians down to the settlements and we will give you some beef-cattle and some
flour. If you are afraid of the tobacco which I send you,

you can let some of your prisoners try it first, and then you will know that it is good. When you get good-natured again, I would like to see you. Don't you think you should be ashamed? You know I have always been your best friend.

Brigham Young.

Walkara didn't intend to give up yet, though he knew it was a futile rebellion. Six years ago, he and his braves could have wiped out the first companies of pioneers, but now he was hopelessly outnumbered. It was not until the end of November that Walkara sent his brother Ammon into the little settlement of Parowan with word that he was ready to make peace.

Brigham Young accepted Walkara's surrender without the slightest show of triumph or scorn for the defeated chieftain. The Mormon leader sent word that he would meet with the Ute in the spring to smoke a formal treaty of peace. Then the Mormons at Fort Harmony returned all Walkara's cattle, which had been impounded at the beginning of the trouble. Walkara accepted his friendly gesture with no show of surprise, though he well knew how other white men had reacted to Indian hostilities. In his raids over the entire West, he had heard and seen much of the white man's retaliatory measures against hostile Indians.

In the spring, Brigham went south with several apostles, a military escort and a following large enough to salve the wounded prestige of the Ute. With pomp and ceremony the Mormon leader went to Walkara's camp on Chicken Creek. At first the Ute was sulky and refused to talk. But Brigham showed no impatience. With the utmost good nature he awaited the surly chieftain's pleasure. When at last Walkara was ready, the great council was held.

In addition to his own followers, Brigham had with him two Indian chieftains, Kanosh, the Pahvant, and Peteetneet,

a Ute; Walkara had his subchiefs, many of them his brothers
or half brothers. His father was said to have left fifty sons
roaming the Utah valleys.

The two groups sat in Walkara's tepee and faced each
other with solemn looks. The presents brought by Brigham
Young were distributed by General Daniel Wells. Among
the gifts was a sack filled with plugs of tobacco.

As soon as the gifts were distributed the parley could
begin. The pipe of peace was passed from hand to hand
around the circle. The discussion of terms went on. Outside
the tepee the trading began, and there was general merrymaking as gifts were distributed and bets laid.

When the conference was over, Brigham Young continued
southward to visit the settlements, as was his custom each
spring. With him went Walkara, now entirely won over. The
Ute chieftain sat beside Brigham Young on the rostrum at
the town meetings. No one would have guessed that a few
short weeks ago the Ute had been determined to wipe out
every Saint.

The only reference Brigham made to his triumph was
when he said, "The Walker War is over. I have brought it
with me."

CHAPTER EIGHTEEN

A DESERTED CITY

➤➤➤-➤➤➤-➤➤➤-➤➤➤-➤➤➤-➤➤➤-➤➤➤-➤➤➤-➤➤➤

Brigham Young had said, "If they'll just give us ten years unmolested in these mountains, we shall not ask odds of anyone!" It began to look as if he was right. The population of the Great Basin was growing with an amazing rapidity.

From the eastern states, from England, Ireland, Scotland, Wales and the Isle of Man; from Norway, Sweden and Denmark; from Holland and Germany and France; from the islands in the South Pacific—from every corner of the world came the emigrants, pouring over the "rim" of the Great Basin to fill every glen and valley.

The cost of the journey from Liverpool to great Salt Lake City by ship and ox team was between fifty and sixty dollars. But many who wished to get to the mountains did not have the money to pay transportation for their entire families. Still they were clamoring to come. Brigham felt he must find some cheaper method of transporting these thousands across the plains.

His practical mind found a solution.

"Most of the emigrants walk all the way across the plains," he observed to his first counselor Heber Kimball. "They are permitted only one hundred pounds of luggage per person, and the wagons carry this luggage and the provisions for the journey. Only the sick and the aged and the very young get to ride."

Heber nodded. "That's right, Brother Brigham. My own family and yours walked most of the way."

"Well, then, why can't they dispense with the ox teams and wagons?"

Heber's black eyes regarded his friend. "How would they bring their provisions, then?"

"In handcarts!"

Thus simply was the Handcart emigration proposed and it was eagerly grasped by the impatient Saints in Europe. With the cost of transportation reduced to the utmost minimum, over four thousand Saints left Liverpool that early spring of 1856—more than had ever before left England in a similar period and more than would ever again leave in a few short months. Half of them planned to travel across the plains and mountains in handcart companies.

Iowa City was the great outfitting place. The plan was new; no handcarts had ever been manufactured; the Saints had to build their conveyances right there on the camp ground. The people were in a hurry. Unskilled as wagon-makers, they often used green timber. The only important thing, it seemed to these emigrants, was to have the carts light of weight, and so strength was sacrificed. Many of the carts were fragile and unable to withstand the long, hard journey.

The carts were constructed of two parallel hickory or oak or birch poles, about five feet long and two and one-half inches thick. A flat, box-like affair was built at one end, with a pair of light wheels, one at each side of this "bed." At the other end of the poles was a crosspiece, which served as a handle. Standing between the poles and behind this cross-piece, the person pulled the contraption along. The whole thing weighed only about sixty pounds, and the emigrants were permitted to carry only the minimum of rations for the trip.

The first two companies of some five hundred people left

Iowa City in June. Though the journey was desperately hard, they managed to reach the valley before the end of September. They did not find the long walk too wearisome, and their spirits were kept high by the lively Handcart Song:

> "Hurrah for the Camp of Israel!
>   Hurrah for the handcart scheme!
> Hurrah! Hurrah! 'Tis better far
>   Than the wagon and ox team.
> Our faith goes with the handcarts,
>   And they have our hearts' best love;
> 'Tis a novel mode of traveling
>   Devised by the Gods above!"

Or another favorite:

> "For some must push and some must pull,
>   As we go marching up the hill,
> So merrily on the way we go
>   Until we reach the valley, Oh."

As the first companies came into the valley they were met by Brigham Young and Heber C. Kimball, together with other church leaders and crowds of Saints. Pitts's Brass Band was there, playing triumphant tunes. Brigham was well pleased with his project. The handcart train had made the trip in less time than the ox teams required. Walking gaily along, they had covered as much as thirty-five miles on the best days and had averaged eleven miles a day.

Late in July, nearly two months after the first companies set out, two other companies started from Iowa City. There were more than a thousand people in these two groups, and many felt that it was too late in the season to start on such a long journey. But the Saints were impatient, feeling sure they could reach the valley before winter set in.

They were too optimistic, however. Delayed by accident and sickness, by scarcity of game along the much-traveled route and by their enormous numbers, the unfortunate companies did not reach Laramie until September, with five hundred miles still ahead of them. Rations were so low that workingmen could be allowed only twelve ounces of flour per day; children received only four ounces. And winter came early, filling the streams with icy water, mantling the mountains with snow and adding the hardship of cold to the burden of hunger.

The happy spirit of the first companies could not survive these conditions, and when the old and the weak lay down and died—as many as five in a single night—sorrow was added to the already overpowering misery. Despondent, cold, hungry, the Saints struggled on through icy waters and deepening snows, almost certain they would never set eyes upon their longed-for Zion.

Joseph, Brigham's oldest son, now a handsome young man of twenty-one, was returning to the valley from a mission in the East. He caught up with this unfortunate group and traveled along with them. But when he saw the desperate plight they were in, on foot, in ice and snow and bitter winds, he bade them good-by.

"Be of good cheer and stout hearts," he urged. "I'll ride ahead and send aid back to you."

With an energy almost equal to his father's, Joseph rode as fast as he could make his horse travel. At the first settlement he told his story, obtained a fresh horse and rode on.

When Joseph reached the territory, where small settlements of the Saints were more numerous, his friends tried to get him to stop and rest. They would go on to the city and carry the news to his father. But Joseph had seen the suffering. He felt he was the only one who could properly tell the story. So he traveled on.

Brigham was not often surprised by the arrival of anyone

in the valley. Scouts, friends, travelers generally kept him apprised of what was happening and who was approaching. But when Joseph rode into the yard of his mother's home that bitter October night, Brigham was totally unprepared. He heard the horse's hoofs; heard one of the children shout; and he went to the door. Joseph, almost fainting from exhaustion, slipped from the saddle.

"Father! Father!" he cried, "I have terrible news."

Brigham put his arms about his son's shoulders. "Come inside. You are cold and weak with fatigue. Come in and get warm and eat—and then tell your story."

"It can't wait!" Joseph protested. But he let himself be led into the warm, fragrant kitchen. His mother came forward eagerly, but when she saw her son's face she could scarcely keep back the exclamation of dismay.

"Joseph! You have ridden too far today!" She embraced him and had him sit beside the glowing fire while she bustled about getting food. His brothers and sisters clustered around, wide eyed, eager to hear what the returned missionary had to say.

Joseph could not relax. He turned to his father and began to pour out the story of the handcart companies.

"There are two companies, stranded, freezing to death, Father. Captain James Willie's and Captain Edward Martin's. They'll never make it to the valley unless help goes out at once!"

Brigham listened, his blue eyes dimmed with pain. When the miserable tale was finished he shook his head as if to shake the vision from his eyes. For he had seen only too vividly the disaster his son had painted.

"Tomorrow is Sunday—and conference. I had thought to have you speak to the people, Joseph. But that can wait. I'll preach the morning sermon—and by night we'll be getting things together to go out to those people. And," he laid a hand gently on his son's shoulder, "I want you to be ready to go back with the rescue party—"

Mary Ann, usually silent when Brigham's plans were burdensome to her, couldn't help speaking now.

"He's been gone two years, Brigham. And he's worn out now—"

Joseph spoke quietly, "It's all right, Mother. I'll be ready."

Brigham could scarcely sleep that night. Thoughts of his people exposed to the bitter winter of the prairie and the mountain troubled him. And he was glad when morning came and he stood in the pulpit before a throng of Saints gathered for the October Conference.

He spoke vigorously, "I will give you the subject of my text today. It is this: On this fifth day of October, 1856, many of our brethren and sisters are on the plains with handcarts, and probably many are now seven hundred miles from this place. They must be brought here. We must send assistance to them. My text will be—to get them here!"

He repeated this emphatically, then went on, "I shall call on the bishops this day—I shall not wait for tomorrow or the next day—for sixty good mule teams and wagons. I do not want to send oxen. I want good horses and mules. I want forty good young men who know how to drive. And I want twenty-four thousand pounds of flour to send out to those starving people."

He dismissed the congregation, dispensed with the usual afternoon meeting. He told his people they would be serving their religion best by going home and getting help ready. The men should begin at once to get the teams and wagons, the flour and men. The women should make ready to receive the sufferers.

"When those people arrive, I do not want to see them put into houses by themselves. I want people with good, comfortable houses to take them in. And I wish the sisters to nurse them. Prayer is good, but when baked potatoes and pudding and milk are needed, prayer will not take their place."

Brigham made his demand with the utmost confidence— and he was not disappointed. During the next two days fifty-one young men had volunteered to drive teams out to rescue the handcart companies. Fifty-four teams had been offered, and also over twenty-six thousand pounds of flour, thirty-one bushels of onions, twelve pounds of dried meat, five bushels of oats, one hundred and six quilts and blankets, fifty-three coats, eight cloaks, fifty-one pairs of trousers, fifty vests, one hundred and thirty-four pairs of boots and shoes, twenty-nine shawls, fifty-one dresses, seventy-two shirts, sixty-seven hoods, one hundred and seventy-four pairs of stockings, seventy-two pairs of socks, nine pairs of mittens, four sacks, one buffalo robe, two overshirts, two chemises, four neckties, thirteen hats and caps, three boys' suits, eight pairs of drawers, fifteen jackets, twelve bonnets, seven shirts, four handkerchiefs, one rug, three yards of linsey-woolsey, two aprons and one pair of gloves had been brought to Brigham to be sent out to help the marooned people.

Early on the morning of the third day the caravan set out, moving as fast as possible, with young Joseph leading the way.

Brigham's prompt and efficient handling of this crisis endeared him more than ever to his people. They knew he was intensely interested in every one of them, even in the Saints he had never seen, but who were making their tortuous way to Zion. They knew Brigham would never stand idly by and see any one of them suffer, if there was any possible way for him to relieve that suffering. And he proved it by bringing in all who were left in the handcart brigade.

The thousands that were pouring into the valley by ox team or on foot were helping to build up the power and strength that Brigham so much desired his people to have.

He encouraged all sorts of skilled laborers, machinists and various kinds of craftsmen to come in. Now the Saints were mining their own ore to make iron. The Indians had showed them where an old lead mine lay, perhaps worked by early Spanish explorers or by some forgotten travelers. So they were making their own bullets. And since the Indians also showed them where they could find the "rock that burns," coal was being mined. The Saints were making bricks and paper and cloth. They were experimenting with the manufacture of sugar. They were, as Brigham was constantly urging them to do, trying to become totally self-sufficient here in their isolated home.

Ever since that second anniversary celebration, July 24th had been observed as a great holiday. In 1857, ten years after their entry into the valley, the Saints planned to have the biggest observance yet. Silver Lake in Big Cottonwood Canyon, about twenty-four miles from Salt Lake City, was chosen as the site of the gigantic picnic.

A few days before the big event, several families went to the lake. They cleared a space for dancing, threw up a willow bowery for shade and shelter and prepared spots for cooking and level sites for tents.

Day by day a few other families drifted in, and by July 23rd everyone who had the means of transportation, or could beg a ride from a neighbor, was making ready to join in the celebration.

Some two thousand Saints accepted the invitation. On July 24th the lovely meadow around the lake was dotted with tents and wagons. A holiday spirit prevailed. Some of the people were fishing; others strolled through the meadows near the lake; still others climbed the steep slopes to gather the Alpine-like flowers. There were dancing and games and feasting. There was rejoicing in the prosperity and happiness that prevailed.

Into this happy gathering rode Elder A. O. Smoot, Judson

Stoddard and the untiring Porter Rockwell. The horsemen
were travel stained and weary, but their attitude and their
haste betrayed the importance of the message they brought.
The United States Army was on the way to the territory
to put down the Mormon rebellion!

During the years since Utah had been made a territory,
the settlers had had various difficulties with the United
States government. Many of the men sent out to take over
federal offices were unworthy representatives of the government. They were often unsympathetic with the people
they were to govern. And they made no effort to understand
or co-operate with these people.

But more than this, the federal officers could not help
seeing that the Mormons loved and respected Brigham
Young. He was not only their governor, he was also president of their church, and they would do almost anything he
wished. The officials, feeling that this was too much power
for any one man to have, wanted to separate the political
and the religious authority. They resorted to harsh and
unfortunate measures while they were in the territory, and
the people reacted in no uncertain manner. One by one,
federal officials were forced to leave the territory.

When they reached the East, these ousted officers began
to circulate all sorts of wild tales about the Mormons and
their leader. They published newspaper and magazine
articles saying that a rebellious kingdom was growing up
in the mountains, which would someday try to overthrow
the national government. They demanded that something
be done to bring this mountain "empire" to its knees.

James Buchanan was inaugurated president in March of
1857, with a cabinet largely hostile to the Mormons. He
immediately appointed a new governor to take Brigham
Young's place in the territory, and named a whole slate of
other federal officers to come in and handle government
affairs. Because of the stories that had been circulated, the

President considered it necessary to have these new officers accompanied by United States troops. He had heard that in no other way would they be permitted to enter the territory.

This was the news the riders brought to the celebrants at Silver Lake. To the Mormons, who had been driven from their homes so many times, the sending of troops meant only that again they were to be herded off of their hard-won property; that their homes and farms and cattle were to be confiscated by the government.

Brigham called his people together and read the message aloud to them. Then he asked, "Will you submit to the entrance of the army? Will you be driven from your homes again? Or will you defend them?"

Old men, young men and even mere boys leaped to their feet, clicked their heels together and shouted, "We will defend! Defend! Defend!"

Brigham smiled. "Proceed with your celebration!"

The question that faced Brigham was what to do. He knew very well that he could, perhaps, wipe out this first contingent of troops. They had to pass through the narrow canyons that led into the city. It would be easy enough to station men on the high bluffs who could rain rocks and bullets down on the advancing soldiers. But this would be merely a delaying movement. More troops would be sent— and more. It would be even more hopeless than Walkara's defiance of the settlers. And yet Brigham could not passively submit to what he and his people felt was an insult.

In September Captain Maurice Van Vliet came on ahead of the troops which had reached Fort Bridger. He came to talk with Brigham Young and see what sort of arrangement could be made. He was received politely, but was told what the Mormon leader had decided to do.

"Our people have been persecuted and robbed in Missouri and Illinois, both by mobs and by state troops, and now the United States government is coming against us. We have determined to resist all persecution at the very commencement. Sir, the troops that are on the march toward Utah must not enter the Great Salt Lake Valley."

Captain Van Vliet smiled grimly. "You may, sir, be able to prevent the small force now on its way here from getting through the narrow defiles of the mountains this year. But it would only mean that the government would send greater forces next spring."

Brigham's lips twisted wryly, but his blue eyes never wavered. "We are aware that such will be the case, but when those troops arrive they will find Utah a desert. Every house will be burned to the ground, every tree cut down and every field laid waste. We have three years' provisions on hand, which we will cache, and then take to the mountains."

That was the desperate measure Brigham and his counselors had decided upon.

They had also decided to keep these first troops out of the valley by harassing them as much as possible. Brigham ordered his guerrilla forces, under the command of Lot Smith and other able leaders, to fire no shot against the government troops. But they were to drive off cattle, tear up bridges, set fire to supply trains and do anything they could to hold the soldiers back.

The territory was placed under martial law, with a well-organized militia in every settlement. The people of Salt Lake moved out of their homes and started south. But they left those homes ready for the match—straw on the floors to make a quick fire if the soldiers came.

The men went into the canyons to set up defenses on the high bluffs that towered over the roads. Here they collected huge boulders which they planned to roll down on the advancing army. Every man, woman and child was thinking of fighting to save their homes. And as always, in times of stress, the Saints began to sing.

Some, saddened at the thought of losing the labor of ten hard years—the homes they now loved passionately—sang soberly:

O, ye mountains high where the clear blue sky
Arches over the vales of the free,
Where the cool breezes blow and the clear streamlets
    flow,
All our fond hopes are centered in thee!
O, Zion! Dear Zion! Home of the free,
In thy temples we'll bend, all thy rights we'll defend,
And our home shall be ever with thee.

Others, more belligerent, went about their work shouting:

Up, awake, ye defenders of Zion!
The foe's at the door of your homes;
Let each heart be the heart of a lion,
Unyielding and proud as he roams.
Remember the wrongs of Missouri;
Forget not the fate of Nauvoo;
When the God-hating foe is before ye,
Stand firm and be faithful and true.

While this was going on in Utah, the good friend of the Mormons, Colonel Thomas Kane, was busy in their behalf in Washington. Colonel Kane's father had been a high government official, and the officer himself had enough authority and prestige to get the ear of President Buchanan. He obtained a message from the President direct to Brigham Young. Then, though he was ill, he hastened to Utah. Sailing from New York in January of '58, he crossed the Isthmus of Panama, reached California and came to the territory by way of the southern route. It was a long, difficult journey, but the safest way to reach the mountains in the winter. And it was undertaken through friendship only, for Colonel Kane received no recompense, not even his expenses.

Colonel Kane delivered his message to his friend Brigham, and then he acted as an emissary from President Young to the troops at Camp Scott. With the troops was Alfred Cumming, the newly appointed territorial governor. Through Colonel Kane's efforts an understanding was reached. Governor Cumming, accompanied by Colonel Kane, proceeded to Salt Lake City. There the new territorial head was received with courtesy and taken to the most comfortable quarters in the city. Brigham Young handed over the territorial seal and all official records. He was no longer governor.

However, it was impossible to stop the advance of the troops now marching toward the valley under General Albert Sidney Johnston. Brigham requested that the troops be not permitted to camp in the city or near any of the settlements. General Johnston, wishing to comply as far as possible with Brigham's wishes, issued orders to his men. He forbade any acts of vandalism or any retaliatory measures for the discomforts they had suffered at Mormon hands during the past winter.

Late in June the soldiers marched out of the canyon and into the city. Down the broad South Temple Street they marched, bands playing and flags flying. But before they had gone very far, they felt the oppressiveness of the silent, deserted city. No crowds stood along the sidewalks to cheer the troops; no flags waved from the buildings; no stores displayed decorated fronts and windows. It was like a city of the dead. The bands faltered and became silent. Only the rumbling of the wagons, the jangling of harness and the shuffle, shuffle of the marching feet could be heard. The soldiers, awed at the emptiness of the beautiful city, marched on along the wide street, never stopping, past Brigham

Young's silent house, past the temple block with its rock wall and on through the city to the banks of the Jordan River.

They made camp that night beside the Jordan, and a few days later moved on to a site thirty miles south of the city and on the western side of the river. There they established Camp Floyd.

When Brigham, who had moved south to Provo with his people, saw the soldiers settled in their camp away from any city, he returned to his Salt Lake home. The other Saints followed. By mid-July the city beside the Great Salt Lake was bustling again. The Mormon war was over and Governor Cumming was managing the territorial business.

CHAPTER NINETEEN

JOSEPH! JOSEPH!

➤➤➤-➤➤➤-➤➤➤-➤➤➤-➤➤➤-➤➤➤-➤➤➤-➤➤➤-➤➤➤-➤➤➤

Now that the "Utah War" was over and Brigham had
been relieved of his duties as governor, he could turn his
whole attention to building up Zion. The two great projects
dearest to his heart were the building of the Salt Lake
Temple and the bringing of Utah territory into the Union
as a state.

The temple would symbolize the solidity and permanence
of the new kingdom. Statehood would set the nation's seal
of approval upon his people. And Brigham wanted this. For
though he had said over and over again that they wished
to get as far from the States as possible, he was really intensely devoted to his country. The harsh things he said
in irritation were more the expression of his grievance at
being, as he felt, cast out, than any declaration of disloyalty.

But he wanted statehood on his own terms; that is, he
wanted to be accepted with his religion in its entirety, and
this was going to prove impossible of attainment. Brigham
was not to live to see the fulfillment of either dream. The
temple was not finished until sixteen years after Brigham's
death. Statehood was not granted until 1896, after the Saints
had relinquished polygamy.

The cornerstone of the temple had been laid on April 6,
1853, and since then the work had progressed spasmodically
as the people had time to devote to it, for the labor was
largely voluntary and had to be done when men were free

from the fields. The great stone blocks had to be dragged, one at a time by four-yoke ox teams from Little Cottonwood Canyon, twenty-six miles south of the temple site.

But this work was progressing and Brigham watched it with satisfaction.

He was also satisfied with his system of colonies. He had planned to have Mormon settlements one day's journey apart all the way from the northern part of the territory to the Pacific Coast. Thus any Saint wishing to travel to the coast for supplies could stay overnight, every night, with his own people.

Down through the territory the string of settlements was fairly well set up and others were planned. And in addition to these basic communities, Brigham had other settlements at strategic places. Wherever he decided it would be wise to have a town, he sent colonizers out to that place. Keeping in mind the building up of Zion, Brigham looked on this colonizing as a religious duty of his people. He emphasized this aspect by sending men on missions to the various areas. Thus there was the Indian Mission, to help the Lamanites in southern Utah; the Muddy Mission, to develop farms along the Muddy River far to the south and on the route to Los Angeles. There was the Dixie Mission, to settle along the Virgin River where grapes and pomegranates and other semitropical fruits and also cotton could be raised. The Iron Mission developed the iron mines, and so on.

And now Brigham settled down to a fairly systematized life—that of a venerated leader of a growing people. He kept a careful eye on everything in the territory, but he had the time and the influence to try out a few pet social theories here and there.

Most valuable of these, to his people, was his insistence on their planting the very best types of seed, breeding only the best cattle and horses and sheep, and the developing of farms through the use of irrigation. When the Saints had faced the long trek west, Brigham had told them, "Carry with you only the best seeds and animals. It is folly to transport inferior plants and animals so far. Take the best." And, following that precept, he had imported into the territory the finest Merino sheep from California and New Mexico, the best horses and cattle.

Because only through irrigation could farms be successful, the Saints were more or less forced into a degree of cooperation seldom found in other areas. As soon as they settled in a new region the irrigating ditches had to be built; turns with the water must be determined; perhaps a small reservoir had to be established. And as everyone had the same interest in these projects, everyone went to work on them together.

Ever since Brigham had gone to Kirtland, where, under the influence of Sidney Rigdon a sort of communal life had been tried, he had toyed with the idea of working out a completely communal life in his settlements. So now that he had time, he established a few such communities—in the north and the center and the south of the territory. In these, there was no private ownership. Everyone did the work he was best fitted for and drew from the common store whatever he needed.

Each year Brigham made a trip from one end of the territory to the other, looking over the settlements, settling disputes and blessing the people. These journeys were triumphant processions, with the people coming out to meet their leader as he rode into town. The children were dressed in their best, carrying garlands and painted mottoes, and they sang songs written especially for their hero.

In some of the settlements Brigham maintained a home with one of his wives and families there, so that he had a loving welcome and a place to stay. At his home in St. George, in the balmy Utah Dixieland, Brigham would spend the coldest months of the winter. And in the towns where he had no home, he was received with open arms. His people felt highly honored if President Young would stay overnight with them, partake of their food and comfort them with his presence.

Because of these annual trips, Brigham knew his territory intimately. And he loved it all. But there was never any place for which he had the same deep affection he felt for his Salt Lake City home.

When Salt Lake City had first been planned, each of the church leaders had selected his "inheritance"—the property which was to be his own in this new Zion. Brigham had chosen a ten-acre plot just east of the temple site. The log and adobe houses where his family had first been sheltered had now given way to houses built on or near that block.

Brigham's family was now very large and required more than one house. On his property he had had several fine houses erected. There was the Lion House, built from a design furnished by Brigham himself. The long, two-story building took its name from a stone lion which crouched above the first floor portico. Twelve of Brigham's families usually lived in this house.

Next to this and adjoining it was the small building where the Mormon leader had his offices and his own bedroom. On the other side of the office building was the Beehive House. This was a large, square building with a beehive surmounting its cupola. It was built in 1852 and held large, beautifully furnished rooms, where the family's entertaining was done. This house was "home" for several of Brigham's wives and children.

Along the street to the east, in the White House, lived Mary Ann, known throughout the territory as Mother Young.

The entire estate was protected by a high cobblestone wall, built partly as protection against the Indians, partly as an example for his people in the more isolated settlements, but mostly as a project to give work to needy laborers. Above the main entrance to the estate was a high arch on which perched a large wooden eagle with its wings outspread.

This was Brigham's home during the greater part of the year, and he loved it with a deep and abiding love. His wives, his children, his homes and his gardens were matters of pride, not only to Brigham, but to the whole territory. The Salt Lake paper, the *Deseret News,* often carried such items as "President Young's peach trees are in blossom now," or "President Young's garden yielded a cucumber eighteen inches long."

Brigham, now approaching old age, had lost none of the forthright expression, none of the clearness of eye, that he had shown as a younger man. True, he now wore his graying hair cut shorter and brushed back from his high forehead. A curly beard edged his firm jaw. His face was still mobile in expression. He could smile wryly or chuckle wholeheartedly. His blue eyes could quell an enemy or win the confidence of a child.

About the Mormon leader was an air of scrubbed cleanliness and ruddy health, even though he often suffered from colds and rheumatism. He dressed formally, in dark broadcloth suits, cut to a somewhat older fashion. He did not think it seemly for man or woman to chase after each new fad. In the summertime he wore light-colored prunella suits.

Brigham's home, his gardens, his family were the models for the whole territory, and with good reason. Large as his family was, it set an example of good behavior, of family loyalty and love. The household duties were organized and apportioned out to those who could best handle them.

He still enjoyed dancing and music. One of the first large buildings erected in the city was the Salt Lake Theatre, for many years known by the Saints simply as "the Theatre." Started in 1861, it was ready for use the next year. It was an exceedingly fine theater and to its stage came most of the famous actors and actresses of the time. Often they were entertained in Brigham's own home and were treated so cordially by the Saints that they returned again and again.

Home theatrical companies were organized, and Brigham's older children took part in the plays, knowing well that their father would be seated close to the stage, generous with his applause if they did well.

Even earlier than the theater, the Social Hall had been erected half a block from Brigham's estate. Here dances and socials and plays were presented. Every entertainment was opened and closed with prayer, and often interrupted for the singing of hymns.

Brigham frowned on "round dancing," but he was always first on the floor for a square dance or cotillion, and his followers waited for him to lead out. As soon as the music started, Brigham would cast his eye about the room, decide on which wife he would dance the first set with (he was careful to give each in turn this honor) and would step over to where she sat. With a courtly bow he would ask her formally for the pleasure of that dance. And then, stepping lively, smiling, perhaps beating time a bit with one hand, he would move out onto the floor and the dance would begin.

Brigham had the happy faculty of making each member of his family feel that he or she was especially loved. Little Clarissa, daughter of Lucy Decker, had a certain little task that she loved. Her mother lived in the Lion House, where Brigham took his breakfast, and it was the little girl's happy privilege to tie a napkin over her father's beard when he sat down to the table, so that no crumb would drop onto the soft, curling hair of which her father was very proud.

Young Don Carlos complained that he hated school, so his father took him out of the classroom and set him to driving mules up the canyon to get wood for the tabernacle floor. The boy soon decided he would rather go to school, and when he was sure of this, Brigham sent him back to the classroom.

Brigham's older daughters—ten of them—were so handsome and modish that they set the style for the whole territory. The people affectionately called them the "Big Ten," and everywhere they went they were greeted by affectionate smiles and words.

Brigham was so proud of these handsome daughters that he had a special sleigh built for them. Its sides were carved to represent swans, and it was drawn by six beautifully matched horses. All ten of the young ladies could ride in this sleigh, which was named the "Julia Deane," after a famous actress of the day, whom Brigham greatly admired. With the harness bells jingling merrily, the girls laughing gaily, the "Julia Deane" was a pretty sight on winter days, dashing along the wide, snowy streets.

Likely as not it would be taking the Big Ten, with a few younger brothers and sisters tucked in here and there, out to the "farm" for a party. The farm was a large tract of land south of the city, with a fine adobe house and a mill. A huge brick oven was used for baking the bread, which was famous all over the city. Hot bread, butter and molasses formed a favorite snack at these family parties, and candy pulling, corn popping and dancing were the chief amusements.

Brigham was not the only one who had abandoned the first huts built in the fort. All the other church leaders now had beautiful homes. Some were so elegant that visiting celebrities did not hesitate to call them mansions. And there were plenty of celebrities—not only the famous actors and actresses, but lecturers, newspaper men and artists, glad to break the long journey with a stopover in Salt Lake.

Curiosity was often the main reason for such a stopover, and the visitor was not always tactful, not even courteous.

One of them, asking boldly to see Brigham's wives, was met by a cool stare.

"They are not on exhibition, sir!" Brigham said.

But others came to see the marvelous city, whose fame had spread across the nation, and to pay honest tribute to the man who had led his people across prairie and river to the scarcely known valley and established a thriving empire there.

Brigham greeted them all courteously, but with a keen understanding of the motives that brought them. To those who came in honest friendliness he was proud to show his city with its churches and schools and public buildings. The unique tabernacle, with its beams tied together with rawhide strips, was one of the sights he pointed to with great pride. The great domed roof, unsupported by any central pillars, was a marvel to the visitors. It so caught sounds that one could stand at one end of the huge auditorium and plainly hear a whisper or a pin dropped at the other end.

Brigham was proud to show his people working steadily at building their great new temple. The gray walls were rising, nearly twenty feet high they were now, and Brigham hoped to live to see this great temple completed.

Brigham was proud of the church newspaper, the *Deseret News*, the first newspaper in the Mountain West. He was proud of his theater, of the Deseret University, of the new phonetic alphabet he had helped to work out, of the co-operative store housed in a fine building, of the cleanliness, prosperity and beauty of his city.

Brigham spent his seventy-sixth birthday, June 1, 1877, quietly at home. There was a family birthday dinner, with his living brothers Joseph, Phineas and Lorenzo seated beside the leader, while his wives and children surrounded him.

Six weeks later he made his last trip to visit the settlements he loved so well. He went northward, this time, to organize Boxelder Stake, one of the units of Mormon church organization. When he returned, he told his family that he did not feel well, but thought it was nothing serious.

The family held its usual evening prayer service together. Then Brigham took his lighted candle and went to his bedroom.

"I think I shall go now and take my rest," he said as he left the family group.

Just before midnight he was seized with acute pain and nausea. This occurred on a Thursday night, and his illness continued until the following Wednesday, August 29, 1877. On that morning the physician advised the family that the illness was probably fatal, and his brothers, wives and children gathered in the home. Brigham was lifted from the canopied bed in the alcove of his bedroom and placed on a bed near the open window. There his family could surround him in his last hour.

As he was placed on this bed, Brigham, who had been under opiates to relieve the intense pain, seemed to revive. He opened his eyes, looked out toward the rising temple walls and exclaimed, "Joseph! Joseph! Joseph!"

His voice died away and a look of peace settled upon his features. His family knelt and bowed their heads. The beloved father, the great leader, the "Mormon Moses," greatest colonizer of his age, was dead.

BIBLIOGRAPHY

Anderson, Edward H. LIFE OF BRIGHAM YOUNG. Bureau of Information, Salt Lake City, 1915.

Bancroft, Hubert H. HISTORY OF UTAH. History Co., San Francisco, 1890.

Bailey, Paul. WALKARA, HAWK OF THE MOUNTAINS. Westernlore Press, Los Angeles, 1954.

Cowley, M. F. PROPHETS AND PATRIARCHS OF THE CHURCH OF JESUS CHRIST OF LATTER-DAY SAINTS. Pub. Ben E. Rich, Chattanooga, Tenn. 1902.

Crockwell, J. H. PICTURES & BIOGRAPHIES OF BRIGHAM YOUNG & HIS WIVES. J. H. Crockwell, Salt Lake City.

Deseret News from 1850 to 1877. (Excerpts from)

Evans, John Henry. 100 YEARS OF MORMONISM. Deseret News Press, Salt Lake, 1905.

Gates, Susa Young and Widtsoe, Leah D. THE LIFE STORY OF BRIGHAM YOUNG, HEART THROBS OF THE WEST, Kate B. Carter, ed. Vols. 1 to 12. Daughters of the Utah Pioneers, Salt Lake City, 1929 to 1951.

Hunter, Milton R. BRIGHAM YOUNG THE COLONIZER. Deseret News Press, Salt Lake City, 1940.

Nibley, Preston. BRIGHAM YOUNG. Deseret News Press, Salt Lake City, 1936.

Roberts, Brigham H. HISTORY OF THE MORMON CHURCH. Salt Lake City.

———LIFE OF JOHN TAYLOR, Salt Lake City.

Spencer, Mrs. Clarissa Young and Harmer, Mabel. BRIGHAM YOUNG AT HOME. Deseret News Press, Salt Lake City, 1947.

Stenhouse, Thomas B. H. ROCKY MOUNTAIN SAINTS. Salt Lake City, 1879.

Utah State Historical Society Publications. Vols. 1 to 22. Salt Lake City, 1928-1954.

Werner, M. R. BRIGHAM YOUNG. Harcourt-Brace & Co., New York, 1924.

Whitney, Orson F. LIFE OF HEBER C. KIMBALL. Stevens & Wallis, Salt Lake City, 1945. (First published 1888).

Young, Brigham. Autobiography. Millennial Star, England, Vol. XXV. 1863. DISCOURSES OF BRIGHAM YOUNG, Edited and arranged by John A. Widtsoe. Deseret Book Co., Salt Lake City, 1925.

INDEX

Abraham, 74
Adamic Tongue, 38
Allen, Capt. James, 101, 104, 107
Anti-Mormons, in New York, 37; in Missouri, 42-44, 51-55; in Illinois, 85-88
Apostles, Quorum of Twelve named, 45-46; Brigham Young assumes presidency of, 53; sent to England, 60; duties of, 71-72; hold Keys of Kingdom, 75-79; to lead Saints, 80; organize for new work, 81-84

Barlow, Israel, 62
Bear River, 134, 153
Beaumont, Charles, 125
Beehive House, 182
Bement, Elder, 74
Benbow, Jane, 67
Benbow, John, 67, 68
Bible, 13, 18, 117
Big Cottonwood Canyon, 172
Big Elk, 108, 109
"Big Ten," 185
Bigler, Henry, 147
Boggs, Gov. Lilburn, 53, 54
Bordeaux, James, 126
Box Elder Stake, 187
Brannan, Samuel, 131-134
Bridger, James, 128, 129, 130-31
Buchanan, Pres. James, 193

California, 116, 127, 131-132
Carthage, Illinois, 75, 85, 87
Chariton River, 100
Chicken Creek, 163
Church of Jesus Christ of Latter-day Saints, Doctrines, 25-31, 39, 157; organization, 36; leaves New York, 37; in Missouri, 42-44; organization completed, 44-46; troubles in Ohio, 47-50; troubles in Missouri, 51-55; membership, 85; troubles in Nauvoo, 85-88; abandons Nauvoo, 88-89; at Winter Quarters, 110-117; President named, 145-146; abandons Winter Quarters, 147; moves West, 148 et seq.
Clark, Gov. James, 99
Clayton, William, 121, 122, 124, 125

Colonization Plan, 180
Commerce, Illinois, 54
Communal Life, 41, 181
Conference, LDS Church, 45-46, 89-90, 115, 116
Council Bluffs, 101
Covenant of Mutual Aid, 53, 112
Crickets, 150-52
Crooked River, Missouri, 53
Crow, Robert, 126
Cumming, Gov. Alfred, 177
Cumorah, Hill of, 27

Deane, Julia, 185
Deseret, defined, 154; Alphabet, 186; News, 183, 186; State of, 154; University, 186
de Smet, Father Pierre J., 113
Digger Indians, 114
Dow, Lorenzo, 14-16
Donner Party, 132-133
Duzett's Military Band, 106

Elkhorn River, 117
Emigration to West, 83, 115, 117-119, 120-135, 165-171
Ensign Peak, 138

Far West, Missouri, 49, 51, 147
Fearnought, Captain. See Patten, David W.
Fillmore, Pres. Millard, 160
First Presidency of LDS Church, 71
Floyd, Camp, 178
Ford, Gov. Thomas, 77
Fort Bridger, 174
Fort Buenaventura, 153
Fort Laramie, 125, 126, 168
Fremont, Capt. John C., 113, 128, 130

Garden Grove, 90, 100
"Gathering" of Saints, to Kirtland, 39; to Missouri, 49-50; from Great Britain, 68-70
Gold, discovered in California, 147; Saints urged to refrain from hunting, 153
Goodyear, Miles, 153
Grand River, 100, 101
Great Basin, 113, 114, 154, 165

189

191

Yerba Buena, California, 132
Young, Abigail Howe (Brigham's mother) 11-16, 18, 22
Young, Brigham, Description, 9, 81-82, 117, 183; birth, 11; attracted by music, 16-17; hears story of Moses, 18; boyhood idea of religion, 20-21; to be apprenticed, 22; wife and daughter, 24-31; first sees Book of Mormon, 25; hears of Joseph Smith, 27-28; baptized, 30; ordained an elder, 31; cabinet maker, 32; mission to Indians, 33; goes to Kirtland, 33; meets Joseph Smith, 35; has gift of tongues, 38; mission to Canada, 39; leads group to Kirtland, 39; works on temple, 41; marries Mary Ann Angel, 42; in Zion's Camp, 42-44; named Apostle, 46; son born, 46; Mission to New England, 46; return to Kirtland, 47; defends Joseph, 48; twins born, 49; leaves Kirtland, 50; in Far West, 51-54; leads Saints to Illinois, 54; president of Quorum of Twelve, 54; hears plans for Nauvoo, 58-59; has malaria, 60; leaves for British mission, 62; raises money in New York, 63; takes charge of British Mission, 65; Success in England, 69-70; returns to Nauvoo, 71-72; heads campaign for Joseph Smith as President, 74; hears of Joseph's death, 75; returns to Nauvoo, 77; proposes Apostles head Church, 80; upheld by vote, 80; plans for Church, 81-83; work in Nauvoo, 83-86; plans exodus West, 87; leaves Nauvoo, 91-92; organizes camp, 95-96; builds way stations, 101; provides Mormon Battalion, 102-105; moves to Omaha land, 108-109; sends aid to Nauvoo, 112; leaves Winter Quarters, 119; gives rules for journey, 120, 124-125; builds ferry on Platte River, 127; meets Jim Bridger, 129-130; meets Sam Brannan, 130-133; decides on Salt Lake Valley, 133; stricken with mountain fever, 134; sees Valley, 135; enters Valley, 136; advises treatment of Indians, 137, 157; names Jordan River, 139; chooses site of Salt Lake Temple, 139; returns to Winter Quarters, 143; made President of the Church, 146; abandons Winter Quarters, 147; reproves Saints for bickering, 149; welcomed by Saints in Salt Lake Valley, 150; governor of State of Deseret, 154; asks ten years of peace, 155; governor of Utah Territory, 160; Superintendent of Indian Affairs, 160; treatment of Chief Walkara, 161-163; sends aid to handcart companies, 169-172; defies U. S. troops, 175; leaves Salt Lake City, 177; returns, 178; develops Utah Territory, 180-182; home and family, 181-185; death, 187.

Young, Brigham, Jr., 49, 88, 95-96, 144
Young, Clara Decker, 117
Young, Clarissa, 184
Young, Don Carlos, 184
Young, Elizabeth, 24
Young, Fanny, 11, 13, 26
Young, Harriet Decker, 117
Young, John (Brigham's father), 11, 17, 22-23
Young, John Jr., 9, 33, 40, 44, 186
Young, Joseph (Brigham's brother), 9, 33-40, 44, 186
Young, Joseph (Brigham's son), 46, 56, 57, 61, 95-96, 118, 144, 168-169
Young, Lorenzo Dow, 19, 117, 186
Young, Louisa, 12, 15
Young, Lucy Ann Decker, 74, 88, 118, 184
Young, Mary, 49, 55
Young, Mary Ann Angel, 42, 49-50, 55-58, 61, 71, 88, 95-97, 106, 118, 145, 182
Young, Miriam, 24-31
Young, Nabby, 12, 15
Young, Nancy, 12
Young, Phineas, 9-16, 20, 25, 186
Young, Rhoda, 12
Young, Susanna, 12
Young, Vilate, 28

Zion, 37, 42, 66, 81, 92, 115
Zion's Camp, 42-44
Zion's Ensign, 138

192

About the Author

OLIVE BURT, like her ancestors, was born in Utah and has lived there all her life. She majored in English at the University of Utah, taught English in high schools in Wyoming and Utah. Later she joined the staff of the Salt Lake *Tribune* as children's feature editor. In 1947 she became magazine editor of the *Deseret News* and traveled all of the eight" mountain-west" states collecting material. Out of this grew an interest in history and the writing of books for young people. She has more than twenty books to her credit, many of which have won awards for their contribution to young people's literature.